Kuiter, Rudie H.: Fairy & Rainbow Wrasses and Their Relatives - A Comprehensive Guide to Selected Labroids

First English language edition 2002

Published by TMC Publishing, Chorleywood, UK

Responsibility of text and taxonomic decisions: Rudie H. Kuiter.

Production: IKAN UW-Archives.
Print: Grupo M & G Difusión S.L.

TMC Publishing
Solesbridge Lane,
Chorleywood, Herts WD3 5SX
United Kingdom

Tel: +44 (0) 1923 284151   Fax: +44 (0) 1923 285840
Email: info@tmc-publishing.com
Website: www.tmc-publishing.com

ISBN 0-9539097-2-7

The Marine Fish Families Series

Fairy & Rainbow Wrasses and their relatives

A Comprehensive Guide to Selected Labroids

Rudie H Kuiter

TMC

publishing

TMC Publishing, Chorleywood, UK

ACKNOWLEDGEMENTS: My thanks to those who assisted in taxonomy, supplied information, especially Martin Gomon and Jerry Allen, and to the contributing photographers. Jerry Allen, Neville Coleman, Tomonori Hirata, Roger Steene and Phil Woodhead generously supplied many photographs. Hiroyuki Tanaka was very helpful in assisting with supplying material of several Japanese photographers.

Photo-credits: Contributing photographers are credited in the captions. All other photographs and illustrations are by the author.

TABLE OF CONTENTS

INTRODUCTION

The family Labridae, its members commonly known as wrasses, is one of the largest and most important groups of fishes on the reef. Over 460 species are recognised around the world, belonging to more that 65 genera, but the taxonomy and relationship between the various genera and species continue to be scrutinised. Many species are closely related and have only recently evolved. Species in such genera as *Paracheilinus* and *Cirrhilabrus* often display different colour patterns over their geographical range and in some cases it may be difficult to decide on their taxonomic status. There are several distinct groups that presently are divided into tribes or subfamilies. In this work, the various labrid genera are grouped together into subfamilies. Since the number of species in Labridae is very large, it is not possible to include them all in a single volume of the Marine Fish-Families Series, whilst maintaining comprehensive coverage of all the groups at the same time. One can be forgiven for selecting the pretty ones first, but they represent the smaller species that are commonly found in the aquarium and are of more interest to divers or researchers. Included are some of the subfamilies and selected large genera of other groups that are of interest from the diver/aquarist's perspective. Some of the most spectacular genera such as *Paracheilinus* and *Cirrhilabrus* belong in the subfamily Cheilininae. The males display with brilliant colours and most species have a small maximum size, reaching about 10 cm. Such fishes are ideal for the home aquarium, but this subfamily also includes the largest wrasses. The largest of all is *Cheilinus undulatus*, well known by divers as the Napoleon Wrasse, which reaches over 2 m in length and has a massive weight of almost 200 kg. Most wrasse genera are placed in Julininae, including genera such as *Anampses, Coris & Halichoeres,* many of which are commonly seen in shallow tropical reef species. Wrasses that are popularly known as hogfishes and tuskfishes are placed in Hypsigenyinae and the specialised cleaner wrasses in Labrichthyinae. The specialised sand wrasses, such as razor fishes are the Novaculininae and these 3 groups will be covered in the second volume on labroid fishes.

The name Labridae was derived from *Labrus,* the earliest named genus in the family. *Labrus* refers to the lips *(labrum)* and whilst the popular name, wrasses, is used in English, their name in other languages usually means 'lip-fishes'. Many species have thick fleshy lips, which is one of the aspects that separates them from the closely related families Odacidae and Scaridae. Other important differences are in dentition. In Labridae most species have separate canines and crushing teeth, whilst in Odacidae and Scaridae these are mostly fused. Wrasses are further characterised by the presence of a single dorsal fin, not obviously notched (except some razor fishes that have separate spines on top of their head), with the spinous part usually longer than the soft-rayed section.

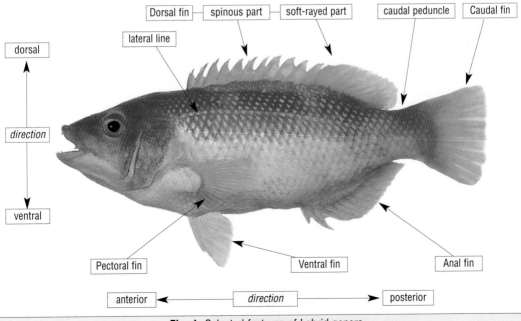

Fig. 1. Selected features of Labrid genera.

LABROIDS

Labroids are a suborder of Perciformes, the largest order of fishes that includes most of the fish families we see on the reef, such as damselfishes, butterflyfishes and angelfishes or the snapper groups. The labroids comprise 3 families, of which the wrasses, LABRIDAE, are the most numerous with over 460 species. They are widespread globally and representatives are found in all but the coldest seas. The next largest group, the parrotfishes, family SCARIDAE, with 10 genera and about 90 species, occur globally in tropical waters, whilst the cales, family ODACIDAE, comprising 4 genera and 12 species, are restricted to temperate or subtemperate seas of Australia and New Zealand.

Labroids are characterised by having a continuous dorsal fin in which the spinous and soft parts are joined; anal fin is headed by 3 spines; jaws with conical, molariform teeth, or fused, beak-like. The various groups are classified by a number of different characteristics, of which the different type of teeth play a major role (Fig. 3). Superficially the odacids are most similar to the wrasses, but apart from their differences in teeth, the odacids have only four rays in the ventral fins versus 5 in wrasses (in one odacid and in one wrasses species the ventrals are completely absent). In addition wrasses have a protractible mouth whilst odacids and scarids do not.

Wrasses are extremely diverse groups and in some cases may look superficially like members of the related families. The odacids live primarily amongst vegetation, and wrasses that occupy weedy habitats may have evolved into similarly shaped and coloured fishes. The different type of teeth and the different number of rays in the ventral fin distinguishes the two families, but such features are difficult to observe in the wild, especially when dealing with juveniles. The odacids look and behave much like wrasses that live in weedy habitats. They have similar diets, feeding on small invertebrates such as crustaceans. Like many of the wrasses, some of the odacids 'clean' other fishes by picking off small parasitic crustaceans, often on particular places on reefs that are easily recognised by their potential customers.

The scarids are usually easily identified as being related to a family by their obvious beak-like mouth that is used for scraping algae from coral bases, rubble or rocks, and some species scrape the corals with living tissue. On average parrotfishes grow larger than wrasses and often form schools or occur in large spread-out numbers on shallow reefs comprising several species. In the process of scraping on coral and rubble they digest a great amount of the coral-skeleton which is pulverised in their gut to sand-like matter. In all they produce an enormous amount of sand and therefore produce an important component of the reef-building process. None of the wrasses species look much like scarids and it is unlikely that they will be confused, except perhaps in the case of juveniles of some species.

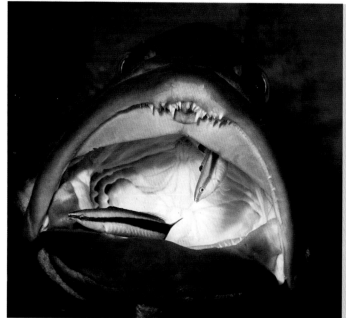

Fig. 2. A pair of cleaner wrasses, *Labroides dimidiatus*, 'at work' in the mouth of a cod, *Epinephelus* sp.

Cleaner wrasses are commonly observed on coral reefs, playing an important role in removing parasites, food stuck between teeth and even attending to wounds. Although many other fishes may perform some sort of cleaning service, it is very common amongst wrasses. Many species will clean as juveniles, but species of *Labroides* have taken this on as a full-time job. Their teeth are modified for the job and adapted to dislodge stubborn parasites. As they are a small species they are able to move about easily in the mouth or gills where parasite and food problems need the most attention.

Fig. 3. Teeth of selected labroid genera of the families LABRIDAE, ODACIDAE and SCARIDAE.
A-C. LABRIDAE. A *Coris*, B *Choerodon*, C *Pseudolabrus*. Wrasses have separate conical teeth in their jaws that are often enlarged in the front or corner of the mouth, especially in large males. A by Gary Bell.

D & E. ODACIDAE. D *Odax*, E *Siphonognathus*. Jaws mostly set with small flat teeth, overlapping in some, forming a cutting edge with recognisable tips, and small canines laterally in lower jaw.

F-H. Scaridae. F *Calotomus*, G *Chlorurus*, H *Scarus*. In parrotfishes the teeth are fused to form a pair of plates in each jaw, its edges sharp and sometimes strongly serrate. Small outward projecting canines are sometimes present in the corner of the mouth of adults (visible in G on the left corner).

Many species are known to change their sex from female to male, accompanied by a change in colouration. The variation in colour between stages and sexes of species is often extreme. Some species show slight variations in colour between juvenile and adult phases, but most wrasses change dramatically with growth. Colouration between male and female can be so different that linking them as being the same taxon is only possible by underwater observation or by keeping them in aquariums. In most cases the identification of species is relatively easy, but it can be difficult when dealing with closely related species or siblings that have similar colour patterns. Colouration is mostly associated with habitat and behaviour, and changes can occur seasonally or can be due to emotional state during times of reproduction. Tropical species may behave differently from temperate ones and such differences are even greater between Pacific and Atlantic labrids, evident in courtship, spawning and nesting behaviour. Many of the wrasse species live in groups of females with a dominating male that claims a section of reef or sand as its territory, but others may occur in mixed groups. Planktivores usually form large schools to feed in the water column, and sex usually plays no role during that time. There are many variations on the sexual behaviour themes, depending on food requirement and abundance of a species. In addition, a species may behave differently from one area to another. It is difficult to generalise on such a diverse family as Labridae with so many species, especially on their behaviour aspects. All known species are diurnal, sleeping in crevices on reefs or burying themselves in the sand during the night. Most wrasses occur on shallow reefs and usually where there are sand or rubble patches. Few have adapted to open substrates, and they are experts in diving into the sea bed, even swimming some distance under the sand by vibrating their body. Diet comprises of small invertebrates, small fishes and zooplankton. This usually changes with growth, and some species are very specific in what they eat. The greatest diversity is found on the tropical Indo-Pacific reefs, but representatives of Labridae occur worldwide in all but the coldest waters. The family is well represented in kelp zones where the species are often amongst the most colourful fishes on the reef.

The largest wrasse is the Napoleon Wrasse *Cheilinus undulatus*. It can reach 2 m in length and weigh up to 200 kg. Some individuals become very tame in popular dive-sites or lagoon moorings where fish are often cleaned on boats and may get an easy meal. The thick fleshy lips, typical for most adult wrasses, are clearly visible in the photograph and it shows the use of the pectoral fin, rather than the other fins, for swimming at an easy pace. The diver above looks comparatively small due to the wide-angle lens used. GBR, Gary Bell.

Cirrhilabrus flavidorsalis. Sangihe Islands, Indonesia. Depth 10 m. Length about 65 mm.
Sexual dimorphism. The male has a distinctive yellow dorsal fin, whilst the female is rather plain and has a pupil-sized black spot on the caudal peduncle. In many species of these fairy wrasses there are great differences in colour between the sexes and males often feature longer fins or filaments, which are displayed during courtship.

SPAWNING AND DEVELOPMENT

Spawning behaviour varies greatly between species and may vary somewhat between different populations of the same species. Most tropical species, if not all, spawn floating eggs that are released near the surface, whilst some temperate species in the North Atlantic have demersal eggs that are produced in nests or amongst seagrasses. There are no known Indo-Pacific species to spawn demersal eggs. Temperate species are seasonal and spawning usually takes place from late winter to early summer, depending on the species and area. Of those species producing demersal eggs, males build a nest amongst gravel or rocks, sometimes adding bits of algae, and some produce sticky eggs that attach to seagrass fronts. Tropical species may breed all year around, but timing is more or less specific, depending on species and abundance or maybe in relation to wet-seasons. Many species spawn at a specific time of the day, usually late afternoon, or the event may be influenced by certain tides. Gathering groups often spawn at special places on reefs. Some form pairs and others may spawn in groups. This behaviour can vary between species, but occasionally a species may do either, depending on the situation or sexual development of males. Usually male wrasses are secondarily derived from functional females. In the case of a male dominating a number of females in a harem-like situation, the largest females are candidates to become the next male when the position becomes vacant. However, in some species there are born males as well as female-derived males. These forms are known as primary and secondary males and they can look quite different in colour. Secondary males are brightly coloured and usually engage in pair spawning, but the usually smaller, drab, primary males may sneak in as soon as the gametes are released. The timing and place of spawning is important for dispersal of the eggs carried by the current to the open sea. They are numerous and small (0.5–1.1 mm in diameter) and hatch usually within 24 hours. Larvae are very small (1.5–2.7 mm long) and have a large yolk sac, developing their mouth and eyes during yolk absorption. The larval stages are mostly transparent and may be pelagic for a number of weeks to about one month. When settling on the substrate they usually measure about 12 mm in length and full pigmentation of the head and body takes place immediately. Post-larval juveniles are usually found alone on reefs, a few species form small aggregations and some species live in algae or seagrasses. During growth, colour and habits can change dramatically. Small juveniles are usually secretive and rely on camouflage or special colouration to avoid or escape predators, but need to feed over larger parts of the sea bed as they grow and this may require colour changes. A species may be bright green when living in seagrasses or green algae, but may need to move to reefs and turn brown or some other more suitable colour or pattern. Some young are marked with ocelli, eye-like markings, on their fins, usually near the tail, which serve to confuse predators. Such features are usually lost in adults that have learned to avoid predators in other ways. The small species reach adult size in one or two years, but the large species grow fast and can reach maturity in only a few more years and it may take as long as 20 years for them to reach maximum size *(Cheilinus undulatus)*. Growth slows dramatically with age and how long some of these fishes live is uncertain. Large fishes usually live longer than small fishes when they are closely related and live in similar habitats, whilst those living in cool temperatures live longer than those in tropical zones. Some of the smaller species of the genus *Halichoeres,* reaching about 15 cm in length and grown from post-larval stages, survived in aquariums for 7 to 8 years.

ABOUT THIS BOOK

This book is part of the Marine Fish Families Series, dealing with species on a global scale. The aim is to create a series of books that comprehensively covers closely related or certain groups of fishes with photographs, as a pictorial guide, for the purpose of identifying species and to find out what is known about them. A volume may comprise a group, or related groups of fishes that belong in a single family, several families, or just part of a family, depending on how small or large such a group is. The first two volumes dealt with the orders of syngnathiformes and acanthuroidei, encompassing the variously related families in these groups. This third volume is on wrasses, but covers only part of the family Labridae, because of the large number of species involved. The sections are written in the series' comprehensive way, including as many species to a genus as possible, or all genera in a subfamily. Some of the very numerous genera, such as the 'catch-all' *Halichoeres*, with large numbers of species in both Indo-Pacific and Atlantic oceans, ranging from tropical to temperate zones, are not included in full. The similar or obviously closely related species from particular areas are all included. A second volume to include other genera of Labridae to make it complete, and the related families of Scaridae and Odacidae, will be produced after the next book in the series (Chaetodontidae). Where possible, each species is illustrated with photographs of different stages and some of the geographical variations are included. In some cases, the same form of a wide-ranging species may be included to show similarities between different, far apart geographical zones. The genera and species are arranged in order of relationship or similarity. Notes on behaviour are primarily based on the author's experience and are included in the species accounts. Aquarium details are mostly generalised in the genus accounts, but some popular species may have additional information. Notes on habitat, size and behaviour will give the reader further information with regards to keeping wrasses. Illustrations are of living fishes and in their natural habitat whenever possible. Additional aquarium material may be used to illustrate colour changes or rarely photographed species in the wild, or a picture of a freshly caught specimen as a last resort, especially when dealing with deep water species that are almost exclusively known from trawls. Pictorial contents pages provide easy and quick-find facilities for the different genera or species complexes. Photographs are captioned with their scientific name, locality, size and the name of the contributing photographer. The genera all have their own general introduction that gives information on gender, type-species, number of species, range and habitat, behaviour and requirements with regards to husbandry, if known.

NAMES

In this book, a species is presented with its current scientific name followed by the original name, author and date. Each species has a common and scientific name. The scientific species name is binomial. The first part is the genus, shared by closely related species, and the second part is the species name, which is unique. The common and scientific names are presented in a coloured box, separate from the main text and immediately recognisable on the page. The text box for each species begins with the original name when it was described, the author, and the date. The genus given there may differ from the one currently used. A species may have been described and placed in a genus that was thought to be correct at the time, but other species that belong in the same genus may have been placed in a different genus. In such cases, the oldest name is valid and the later used name corrected. Some of the included species may have been discovered only recently and are not named scientifically. These are placed in the appropriate genus and treated as 'sp', short for species. Some species were described several times by different authors and sometimes the same author described the male and female as different species. There are almost 1400 nominal wrasse names, involving just over 460 species.

Some species may be known under several common names which may reflect different forms or that they are being used in different countries or trades. When only a few species occur in a certain area, a wrasse may be banded or have stripes etc. and this has resulted in many 'Banded Wrasses'. As this book is written from a world perspective, I have added Australian, Atlantic etc. in front of such names to preserve the original local name that can still be applied Divers may call a species one name and an aquarist may use another for the same species. Scientists often translate the meaning of their scientific name, which may be very confusing for the layman since the name often makes no sense. The use of scientific names as common names is even more confusing and is not encouraged in this series of books. Usually a single name is given for a species. If there is a second well-established name, it may be included in the text. Scientific names help to make sure that we are talking about the same taxon, but in some groups the taxonomy is badly in need of work and names are changing regularly on both generic and species levels. Many of the labrids fall into this category and books such as this will help to sort out much of the confusion with closely related species. Some are currently treated as sub-species, geographical variations and in some cases the different sexes of the same species are not recognised.

SUBFAMILY CHEILININAE - Genera Contents

Paracheilinus 10

Cirrhilabrus 20

Conniella 46

Pseudocheilinus 47

Pseudocheilinops 49

Wetmorella 50

Epibulus 52

Pteragogus 54

Cheilinus 59

Cheilinus 59

GENUS *Paracheilinus* Fourmanoir, 1955

Masculine. Type species: *Paracheilinus octotaenia* Fourmanoir, 1955. A small Indo-Pacific genus with 13 species. Prior to 1977 only one species was known and many were recently described.

1 *P. angulatus* Randall & Lubbock, 1981 **Royal Flasher-wrasse** (p. 18)
2 *P. attenuatus* Randall, 1999 **Seychelles Flasher-wrasse** (p. 17)
3 *P. bellae* Randall, 1988 **Bell's Flasher-wrasse** (p. 17)
4 *P. carpenteri* Randall & Lubbock, 1981 **Carpenter's Flasher-wrasse** (p. 16)
5 *P. cyaneus* Kuiter & Allen, 1999 **Blue Flasher-wrasse** (p. 14)
6 *P. filamentosus* Allen, 1974 **Filamented Flasher-wrasse** (p. 13)
7 *P. flavianalis* Kuiter & Allen, 1999 **Yellow-fin Flasher-wrasse** (p. 15)
8 *P. hemitaeniatus* Randall & Harmelin-Vivien, 1977 **Madagascar Flasher-wrasse** (p. 19)
9 *P. lineopunctatus* Randall & Lubbock, 1981 **Line-spot Flasher-wrasse** (p. 17)
10 *P. mccoskeri* Randall & Harmelin-Vivien, 1977 **McCosker's Flasher-wrasse** (p. 15)
11 *P. octotaenia* Fourmanoir, 1955 **Eight-line Flasher-wrasse** (p. 12)
12 *P. piscillineatus* (Cornic, 1987) **Fairy Flasher-wrasse** (p. 19)
13 *P. togeanensis* Kuiter & Allen, 1999 **Togean Flasher-wrasse** (not included, only known from Tomini Bay, Sulawesi, no photographs of living colours available)

Paracheilinus is part of a group of similar genera, including the more numerous *Cirrhilabrus* and the monotypic *Conniella*. Its members are small and colourful, sexually dimorphic fishes, usually occurring in small to large schools on rock or coral reefs. These fishes are primarily planktivores and during feeding sessions the schools may include a mixture of species from this group, as well as unrelated similar sized planktivores such as anthiid basslets.

After a pelagic larval stage, the juveniles form small groups amongst rubble and stay close to the sea bed. Juveniles and female stages are very similar between different species and in some areas where species mix it is almost impossible to tell them apart. Juveniles and females occur in mixed species groups and in most species males mix or swim in groups of their own. The Red Sea *Paracheilinus octotaenia* behaves differently from the West Pacific species in forming a harem-like arrangement of a territorial male with groups of females. Males derive from females by changing sex.

Paracheilinus filamentosus. Visiting a cleaner wrasse, *Labroides dimidiatus* for an inspection. Flores, Indonesia.

Most *Paracheilinus* species spend the day feeding on tiny creatures that are carefully picked out from the zooplankton. Their eyes have a double lens that enables them to examine the prey in front of them, whilst keeping a general, wide-angle view laterally. During feeding sessions, males occasionally display to other males, flashing some colour and raising their median fins, but as the day progresses the males display more and more. This behaviour changes at the end of the day when females gather on the sea bed and males frantically compete with stunning displays to impress a gravid female. With mixed species it is important that the female recognises her own kind and this may be the reason why males have developed their brilliant nuptial colours. This avoids intentional hybridisation. However when several species are spawning on the same reef section at the same time of the day, the released gametes may mix and cause incidental hybrids. Indeed, when looking for hybrids where species are sympatric, one can find them on a regular basis. The nuptial colours vary over the geographical range of a species and change when other species of the genus are sympatric. The colours intensify when other species are present and develop differently in relation to the other species. This is evident in the widely distributed *P. filamentosus* and such geographical variations may eventually evolve into a complex of several similar species.

Remarks

The members of this genus are beautifully coloured and when fully grown, measure less than 10 cm in total length. This makes them ideal candidates for aquarium displays. In addition, they are much less aggressive than most reef fishes, although in some cases the males may fight. It is best to keep a small number of the same species together and resist the temptation to keep more than one male. Ideally the individuals should be introduced to their new home at the same time. As the male derives from a female, usually the largest individual in a group, it would be better still to start with a group of sub-adults or a small number of juveniles.

All the *Paracheilinus* spp are carnivores, naturally obtaining prey from zooplankton. They are ideally suited for the invertebrate aquarium and can be kept with any other species in such a set-up, especially anthiid basslets. In nature they feed by taking small prey on a regular basis during the day. Most foods comprising of small particles or live shrimp-like crustaceans will be accepted but they need to be fed on a regular basis. Small crevices need to be provided where they can hide or sleep.

Paracheilinus filamentosus and/or *flavianalis*. Juveniles, probably representing two species. Bali, Indonesia.

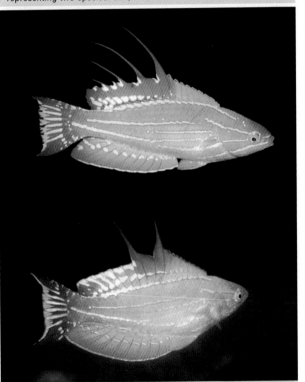

Paracheilinus filamentosus ✕ *flavianalis*. The parent species of these hybrids are both common in Bali, Indonesia. They readily mix and spawn at the same time, and on the same reef sections. The suspended gametes mix in the current which may result in incidental hybrids. These two individuals have the lunate tail of *P. filamentosus* and the anal fin colours of *P. flavianalis*, which are strong characteristics of these species. Hybrids are extremely variable in colour and dorsal filaments, whilst the parent species are more uniform.

11

Paracheilinus octotaenia Fourmanoir, 1955.
Red Sea,

This glorious species is only found in the Red Sea. It occurs over algae-rubble slopes, usually along reef-margins, to a depth of about 25 m. Juveniles swim in small groups close to the seabed and often shelter amongst large soft-coral colonies. Females may swim higher above the substrate in pursuit of zooplankton and a single male is usually in close vicinity. The territorial dispute illustrated in **D** was caused when one of the males was followed by the photographer and it strayed into a neighbour's patch. Easily identified by the short rounded head and colouration. Length to about 9 cm.

A
P. octotaenia. Nuptial male. Egypt, Red Sea. Depth 20 m. Length 9 cm.

B **C**
P. octotaenia. Egypt, Red Sea. Depth 20 m. **B** Adult, probably female, about 85 mm. **C** Juveniles about 45 mm.

D
P. octotaenia. Males, territorial behaviour. Egypt, Red Sea. Depth 20 m. Length 9 cm.

Filamented Flasher-wrasse
Paracheilinus filamentosus

Paracheilinus filamentosus Allen, 1974. Madang, New Guinea.

Widespread Indonesia, PNG, Solomon Islands, and northern Great Barrier Reef. Some geographical variations of nuptial males, influenced by the presence of similar species. It occurs in small to large groups along deep slopes or on slopes at the base of drop-offs, usually at depths of 10 m or more. Generally most common at about 25 m depth. Males readily display to each other or to gravid females to spawn, flashing their colours whilst 'racing' past with erected fins. Males are most colourful where other similar species occur in the same area, such as Derawan where 3 species in the genus swim commonly on the same reefs. Hybrids with several congeners are common. Length to 10 cm, excluding filaments.

A

P. filamentosus. Kalimantan, Indonesia. Depth 10 m. Length 8 cm.

B

P. filamentosus. Flores. D. 15 m. L. 3–5 cm.

C

P. filamentosus. Kalimantan, Indonesia. Depth 12 m. Length 8 cm.

D

P. filamentosus. Solomon Is. Depth 20 m. Roger Steene.

E

F

P. filamentosus. Flores, Indonesia. Depth 25 m. Lengths 8–9 cm.

13

Blue Flasher-wrasse
Paracheilinus cyaneus

Paracheilinus cyaneus Kuiter & Allen, 1999. Banggai Is.

Known from eastern Sulawesi, Lembeh Strait to the Banggai Islands, and Kalimantan. Occurs on sheltered reefs with mixed low corals and algae-rubble. At Derawan on shallow reef crests in small groups at 6–15 m depth. In Lembeh Strait on open, deep sand slopes on patches with mixed low corals and algae-rubble, but mixed with *Paracheilinus filamentosus* which was much more common during observations. Males display with their spectacular metallic blue backs, swimming frantically to impress females, and dorsal filaments sometimes turn white. Length to about 85 mm, excluding tail filaments.

P. cyaneus. Kalimantan, Indonesia. **A** Nuptial male. D. 7 m. L. 65 mm. **B** Female. Depth 6 m. Length 45 mm.

P. cyaneus. Male. Kalimantan. D. 7 m. L. 65 mm.

P. cyaneus. Nuptial male. Derawan. D. 24 m. L. 85 mm.

P. cyaneus. Nuptial male displaying to females (may comprise several species). Kalimantan. Depth 12 m. Length 8 cm.

Yellow-fin Flasher-wrasse
Paracheilinus flavianalis

Paracheilinus flavianalis Kuiter & Allen, 1999.
Scott Reef, Western Australia.

Southern Indonesia from Bali to Flores, southern Moluccen Seas and north-western Australia. Coastal reef slopes and estuaries. Occurs in small groups with numerous females, juveniles and several males, often covering a large section of reef. Males display with bright yellow anal fins and red spikes on the dorsal fin that vary in number from 1 to 4, but usually 2 or 3. Juveniles are secretive when small and form small groups at later stages. Length to 85 mm.

A

P. flavianalis. Male. Bali. Depth 6 m. Length 85 mm.

B

P. flavianalis. Bali. Depth 15 m. Length 3 cm.

C

P. flavianalis. Bali. Depth 6 m. Length 4 cm.

D

P. flavianalis. Bali. Depth 20 m. Length of male 65 mm.

McCosker's Flasher-wrasse
Paracheilinus mccoskeri

Paracheilinus mccoskeri Randall & Harmelin-Vivien, 1977.
Comoro Islands.

Indian Ocean, ranging east to Sumatra. Occurs along reef margins on rubble zones at about 20-40 m depth. Females gather in small groups and males swim around them, often moving from one area to another between groups of females. Small juveniles are secretive and often appear singly or in small groups amongst the rubble. Length to 65 mm.

A

P. mccoskeri. Nuptial male. Maldives. D. 24 m. L. 5 cm.

B

P. mccoskeri. Nuptial male. Sumatra. D. 15 m. L. 65 mm. Jerry Allen.

15

A
P. carpenteri. Male. Philippines. D. 25 m. L. 65 mm. Roger Steene.

Carpenter's Flasher-wrasse *Paracheilinus carpenteri*

Paracheilinus carpenteri Randall & Lubbock, 1981.
Philippines.

Philippines to southern Japan and Palau. Records of this species from Indonesia are based on *Paracheilinus flavianalis* or hybrids *P. flavianalis* X *filamentosus*. *P. carpenteri* is closely related to *P. mccoskeri* and *P. flavianalis* and can be distinguished from both these species by the red ventral fins of fully coloured males or an extra short stripe above the belly. Females occur in small groups, with males usually nearby, on rubble slopes along reef margins to about 40 m depth. Length to 75 mm.

B

C
P. carpenteri. Kochi, Japan. **B** Male, courtship display. D. 24 m. L. 8 cm. **C** Female. D. 24 m. L. 45 mm. **B & C** Tomonori Hirata.

E

F

D
P. carpenteri. Kochi, Japan. **D** Male. D. 24 m. L. 8 cm. **E & F** D. 35 m. L. 20–35 mm (+ *Cirrhilabrus lunatus*). **D–F** Tomonori Hirata.

G

H
P. carpenteri. Males. **G** Male. Palau. Hiroshi Nagano. **H** Kochi, Japan. D. 24 m. L. 8 cm. Tomonori Hirata.

Bell's Flasher-wrasse
Paracheilinus bellae

Paracheilinus bellae Randall, 1988. Marshall Is.

Only known from the Marshall Islands and Palau, Micronesia in the Pacific. Occurs mainly on algae-rubble beds to about 30 m depth. Similar in appearance to *Paracheilinus filamentosus*, but with larger, more slender ventral fins, very long caudal fin filaments, and a body with a series of thin lines and spots, lacking thick stripes. Length to 8 cm, excluding the filamentous caudal fin tips.

A

P. bellae. Male. Palau. Depth 8 m. Length 75 mm. Ryoichi Satoh.

B

P. bellae. Nuptial male. Palau. Depth 20 m. Length 75 mm. Hiroshi Nagano.

Line-spot Flasher-wrasse
Paracheilinus lineopunctatus

Paracheilinus lineopunctatus Randall & Lubbock, 1981. Philippines.

Known from the Philippines to southern Japan. Occurs in small aggregations on rubble slopes adjacent to reefs to about 40 m depth. Identified by the combination of numerous dorsal filaments and rounded caudal fin. Small species, length to about 70 mm.

A

B

P. lineopunctatus. Males. **A** Okinawa, Japan. Kyoh Yunokawa. **B** Philippines. Depth 18 m. Length 65 mm. Rob Myers.

A

P. angulatus. Nuptial male. Kalimantan, Indonesia. D. 12 m. L. 70 mm.

Royal Flasher-wrasse
Paracheilinus angulatus

Paracheilinus angulatus Randall & Lubbock, 1981. Philippines.

Philippines and northern Indonesia. Sheltered reefs with rich coral and algae mix along upper parts of slopes. Occurs in small groups of mixed sexes but mostly females. Identified by the elongated corners of the dorsal and anal fins. Length to 75 mm.

C

P. angulatus. Mabul, Malaysia. D. 10 m. L. 75 mm.

B

P. angulatus. Nuptial males. Kalimantan. D. 12 m. L. 70 mm.

D

P. angulatus. Mabul, Malaysia. D. 10 m. L. 75 mm.

Seychelles Flasher-wrasse
Paracheilinus attenuatus

Paracheilinus attenuatus Randall, 1999. Seychelles.

Only known from the Seychelles and off Kenya, Indian Ocean. It is readily identified by its pointed caudal fin and thin, hair-like filament on the dorsal fin of the male. A deep water species that occurs on rubble slopes near reefs. Length to about 65 mm.

A   B

P. attenuatus. Aquarium imports from Kenya. **A** Nuptial male and **B** female. **A** & **B** Takeshi Aoki.

Fairy Flasher-wrasse
Paracheilinus piscilineatus

Cirrhilabrus piscilineatus Cornic, 1987.
Mauritius.

Only known from Mauritius, in the Indian
Ocean. Occurs in deep water, usually at
depths in excess of 35 m. Males of this
species lack filaments on the dorsal fin
but have a striped pattern that has some
similarities with male *Paracheilinus
mccoskeri* and *P. flavianalis*. The females
and juveniles are distinctly different from
the other species and are readily identified
by their broad reddish-brown band that is
bordered by pale blue lines. Length to
about 7 cm.

A

P. piscilineatus. Male. Mauritius. Collected from 40 m. L. 70 mm. Roger Steene.

B

P. piscilineatus. Juvenile. Aquarium import. Yutaka Niino.

Madagascar Flasher-wrasse
Paracheilinus hemitaeniatus

Paracheilinus hemitaeniatus Randall &
Harmelin-Vivien, 1977. Madagascar.

Madagascar and KwaZulu-Natal, South
Africa. Occurs on reef slopes with rich
invertebrate growth. Dennis King, the
photographer, reported a depth-range
of 25–50 m. In its range it is readily
identified by the colour patterns on the
body and the male by the filamentous
outer rays on the caudal fin. Length to
9 cm, excluding the tail filaments.

A

P. hemitaeniatus. Female and male. KwaZulu-Natal, South Africa. Depth 40 m. Dennis King.

B

P. hemitaeniatus. Male. KwaZulu-Natal, South Africa. Depth 40 m. Dennis King.

Masculine. Type species: *Cirrhilabrus temminckii* Bleeker, 1853. A large Indo-Pacific genus with at least 47 species. Several have geographical forms that appear to represent species-complexes. There are a number of undescribed species and more new ones can be expected from very deep water (~100 m) or remote locations.

1 *C. adornatus* Randall & Kunzmann, 1998 **Debelius' Fairy-wrasse** (p. 30)
2 *C. aurantidorsalis* Allen & Kuiter, 1999 **Orange-back Fairy-wrasse** (p. 27)
3 *C. balteatus* Randall, 1988 **Girdled Fairy-wrasse** (p. 29)
4 *C. blatteus* Springer & Randall, 1974 **Red Sea Fairy-wrasse** (p. 43)
5 *C. claire* Randall & Pyle, 2001 **Claire's Fairy-wrasse** (Deep water, no living colours pictures available)
6 *C. condei* Allen & Randall, 1996 **Black-fin Fairy-wrasse** (p. 29)
7 *C. cyanopleura* (Bleeker, 1851) **Blue-scaled Fairy-wrasse** (p. 25)
8 *C. earlei* Randall & Pyle, 2001 **Earle's Fairy-wrasse** (p. 34)
9 *C. exquisitus* Smith, 1957 **Exquisite Wrasse** (p. 45)
10 *C.* cf *exquisitus* West Pacific (sibling of *C. exquisitus)* **Pacific Exquisite Wrasse** (p. 45)
11 *C. filamentosus* (Klausewitz, 1967) **Whip-fin Fairy-wrasse** (p. 36)
12 *C. flavidorsalis* Randall & Carpenter, 1980 **Yellow-fin Fairy-wrasse** (p. 31)
13 *C. joanallenae* Allen, 2000 (variant of *C. rubriventralis*) **Pulauweh Fairy-wrasse** (p. 37)
14 *C. johnsoni* Randall, 1988 **Johnson's Fairy-wrasse** (no living colours pictures available)
15 *C. jordani* Snyder, 1904 **Flame Fairy-wrasse** (p. 43)
16 *C. katherinae* Randall, 1992 (variant of *C. balteatus)* **Katherine's Fairy-wrasse** (p. 28)
17 *C. katoi* Senou & Hirata, 2000 **Kato's Fairy-wrasse** (p. 39)
18 *C. laboutei* Randall & Lubbock, 1982 **Laboute's Wrasse** (p. 43)
19 *C. lanceolatus* Randall & Masuda, 1991 **Long-tail Fairy-wrasse** (p. 40)
20 *C.* cf *lanceolatus* **Splendid Fairy-wrasse** (p. 41)
21 *C. lineatus* Randall & Lubbock, 1982 **Lavender Fairy-wrasse** (p. 34)
22 *C. lubbocki* Randall & Carpenter, 1980 **Lubbock's Fairy-wrasse** (p. 30)
23 *C. lunatus* Randall & Masuda, 1991 **Crescent-tail Fairy-wrasse** (p. 42)
24 *C. luteovittatus* Randall, 1988 (sibling of *C. solorensis)* **Yellow-streak Fairy-wrasse** (p. 26)
25 *C. lyukyuensis* Ishikawa, 1904 (sibling of *C. cyanopleura)* **Yellow-flanked Fairy-wrasse** (p. 25)
26 *C. melanomarginatus* Randall & Shen, 1978 **Black-margin Fairy-wrasse** (p. 44)
27 *C. morrisoni* Allen, 1999 **Morrison's Fairy-wrasse** (p. 38)
28 *C. punctatus* Randall & Kuiter, 1989 **Fine-spotted Fairy-wrasse** (p. 25)
29 *C. pylei* Allen & Randall, 1996 **Pyle's Fairy-wrasse** (p. 33)
30 *C. randalli* Allen, 1995 (sibling of *C. cyanopleura)* **Shoals Fairy-wrasse** (p. 26)
31 *C. rhomboidalis* Randall, 1988 **Square-tail Fairy-wrasse** (p. 35)
32 *C. roseafasciata* Randall & Lubbock, 1982 **Pink-banded Fairy-wrasse** (New Caledonia, no living colours pictures available)
33 *C. rubrimarginatus* Randall, 1992 **Pink-margin Fairy-wrasse** (p. 32)
34 *C. rubripinnis* Randall & Carpenter, 1980 **Red-finned Fairy-wrasse** (p. 28)
35 *C. rubrisquamis* Randall & Emery, 1983 **Rosy-scaled Fairy-wrasse** (p. 38)
36 *C. rubriventralis* Springer & Randall, 1974 **Social Fairy-wrasse** (p. 37)
37 *C. sanguineus* Cornic, 1987 **Blood-stain Fairy-wrasse** (p. 38)
38 *C. scottorum* Randall & Pyle, 1989 **Scott's Fairy-wrasse** (p. 44)
39 *C. solorensis* Bleeker, 1851 **Red-eyed Fairy-wrasse** (p. 27)
40 *C.* sp 1. **Rosy-fin Fairy-wrasse** (p. 33)
41 *C.* sp 2. **KwaZulu Fairy-wrasse** (p. 38)
42 *C. temminckii* Bleeker, 1853 **Temminck's Fairy-wrasse** (p. 22)
43 *C.* cf *temminckii* - 1 (sibling of *C. temminckii)* **Blue-stripe Flasher** (p. 23)
44 *C.* cf *temminckii* - 2 (sibling of *C. temminckii)* **Peacock Flasher** (p. 23)
45 *C. tonozukai* Allen & Kuiter, 1999 **Tono's Fairy-wrasse** (p. 36)
46 *C. walindi* Allen & Randall, 1996 **Walindi Fairy-wrasse** (p. 31)
47 *C. walshi* Randall & Pyle, 2001 **Walsh's Fairy-wrasse** (p. 35)

Remarks

All members are small and colourful, sexually dimorphic fishes, usually occurring in small to large schools on rock or coral reefs. These fishes are primarily planktivores and during feeding sessions the schools formed may comprise a mix of species of this group, as well as unrelated, similar-sized planktivores such as anthiid basslets. Most species live in shallow depths and in habitats with moderate currents, usually along reef margins or in channels. In many locations there may be several different species of *Cirrhilabrus* present and these fishes often mix, especially when feeding. There are fewer species in deep water, 30–50 m, and usually these occur as a single species that gathers around bommies or swim on rubble slopes below reef-walls. Recently some species have been found in depths to 100 m.

The colouration of juveniles and females is often very similar between different species, especially amongst closely related ones. If the species are not sympatric, they are identified by linking them with the male that has distinctive colouration. However, males are extremely variable within a species and can change colour quickly according to mood such as when fighting with other males or when courting females. Such colour changes vary between populations of the same species occurring in different geographical zones. Colours that are used for courtship display may be intermittent in one area and more permanent in another, seemingly in relation to whether other similar species are present. This has resulted in complicated patterns and difficult species-complexes that may confuse the taxonomist not familiar with each species.

Most species are ideally suited to the home aquarium. As planktivores they require regular feeding during the day. At night they sleep in narrow crevices, and rubble pieces of *Acropora* corals are a good provider of shelter. Most species grow to about 10 cm or less in total length and keeping a small number of the same species is recommended. They are generally not aggressive to other fishes or bottom-dwelling invertebrates, thus making them ideal for the invertebrate aquarium. They are not compatible with other small planktivores such as anthiid basslets and small reef fishes such as dottybacks (Pseudochromidae) or longfins (Plesiopidae).

Cirrhilabrus punctatus. Sydney, Australia.

Newly settled juveniles of most *Cirrhilabrus* spp are characterised by a distinctive white tipped snout. They live secretively amongst rubble and become more adventurous with growth, forming small groups. They graze on the substrate as well as targeting small prey that may swim past such as mysids or zooplankton. Adults of many species form large schools that rise high above the substrate when zooplankton is passing through.

Cirrhilabrus lyukyuensis. Philippines. Depth 24 m. Length about 10 cm. Helmut Debelius.

A group of mostly males, typically for genus, swimming a short distance above the sea bed. Males are distinguished from females by the yellow blotch on their sides. The yellow blotch appears to be permanent in this population, but in many areas it is variable and sometimes only appears in a few individuals. It is closely related to *Cirrhilabrus cyanopleura*, and is part of a complex that includes *C. solorensis, C. luteovittatus* and *C. randalli* that differ in colouration only. In *C. luteovittatus* and *C. randalli* the yellow blotch has extended as a band along the lower sides. The latter species is restricted to off shore islands of north-western Australia where many other reef-species have such colour differences from Indonesian populations, presently regarded as geographical variations. *C. luteovittatus* seems most closely related to *C. solorensis*. A yellow blotch or streak is common amongst reef orientated planktivores such as fusiliers (Caesionidae) and it helps them to stay in touch when feeding above the substrate. Some *Cirrhilabrus*-males change colour when rising from the sea bed to feed. Females usually stay near the sea bed.

A

C. temminckii. Kochi, Japan. D. 25 m. L.10 cm. Tomonori Hirata.

Temminck's Fairy-wrasse *Cirrhilabrus temminckii*

Cirrhilabrus temminckii Bleeker, 1853. Nagasaki, Japan.

Name *Cirrhilabrus temminckii* is used for a species-complex and the true species occurs in southern Japan from Izu Peninsula to the Ryukyu Islands. Variants in Indonesia and western Australia probably represent additional species (see opposite page). Non-excited males are bright red over the back, dusky to red on sides and have white ventrals that are greatly elongated. Nuptial males turn a blue-white over the back. A schooling species, occurring along reef margins to about 25 m depth. Adults may feed high above the substrate on zooplankton, but juveniles remain close to the substrate. Length to 10 cm.

B

F

C. temminckii. Kochi. D. 20 m. L. 30 mm. Tomonori Hirata.

C

G

C. temminckii. Kochi. D. 16 m. L. 35 mm. Tomonori Hirata.

C. temminckii. Nuptial males. Kashiwajima, Japan. D. 20 m. L.10 cm.

D

H

C. temminckii. Kochi. D. 7 m. L. 7 cm. Tomonori Hirata.

C. temminckii. Displaying male. Izu, Japan. Depth 25 m. Length 9 cm.

E

C. temminckii. Male. Izu, Japan. Depth 25 m. Length 9 cm.

I

C. temminckii. Non-excited male. Kashiwajima, Japan.

Blue-stripe Flasher
Cirrhilabrus cf *temminckii* - 1

Indonesia and Malaysian, northern extent of its range uncertain and it may reach southern-most islands of Japan. It differs considerably from *C. temminckii* in colour in female and male stages, especially males during display. Occurs on rocky or rubble reefs in sheltered bays, usually in small groups or mixed with other congeners to about 10 m depth. Length to 10 cm.

A

C. cf *temminckii* - 1. Male. Kalimantan, Indonesia. D. 10 m. L. 10 cm.

B

C. cf *temminckii* - 1. Malaysia. D. 10 m. L. 65 mm.

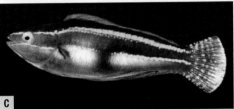

C

D

C. cf *temminckii* - 1. Nuptial male. Bali, Indonesia. Depth 10 m. Length 75 mm.

Peacock Flasher *Cirrhilabrus* cf *temminckii* - 2

Western Australian form with a restricted distribution from the Abrolhos to North-west Cape and Monte Bello Islands. Like the true *Cirrhilabrus temminckii*, males of this form are mainly red over the back and sides, but has dark markings on the side that often show in males of the Indonesian form, as well as a black mark on the pectoral fin base that is absent in the true *C. temminckii*. Occurs in small groups on rocky and rubble reefs to 40 m depth. Length to about 10 cm.

A

B

C

D

C. cf *temminckii* - 2. Female and juvenile. Muiron I., Western Australia. Depth 10 m. Length 60 & 75 mm.

C. cf *temminckii* - 2. Males. Lengths about 10 cm. WA. **A** Shark Bay. Barry Hutchins. **D** Houtman Abrolhos. Collected from 30 m depth. Jerry Allen.

Cirrhilabrus lyukyuensis Ishigawa, 1904. Okinawa, Japan

Southern to northern Indonesia, ranging along Wallace's Line to Bali and southern Sulawesi. Rare in Bali and only occasionally found swimming with *Cirrhilabrus solorensis* and possibly with *C. cyanopleura*. This species is abundant in the Sangihe Islands and males often show a large yellow triangular patch on their sides. In Mabul this colour-patch is more pinkish. Length to 10 cm.

C. lyukyuensis. Male. Iriomote, Japan. Depth 20 m. Length 10 cm.

C. lyukyuensis. Kochi, Japan. **B** Male. Depth 12 m. Length 7 cm. **C** Male, courtship. Depth 8 m. L. 9 cm. **B & C** Tomonori Hirata.

C. lyukyuensis. Japan. **D** Ehime. Female. Depth 16 m. Length 5 cm. **E** Kochi. Female. Depth 10 m. L. 4 cm. **D & E** Tomonori Hirata.

C. lyukyuensis. Male. Mabul, Malaysia. Depth 15 m. Length 10 cm.

C. lyukyuensis. Iriomote, Japan. D. 10 m. L. 40 mm.

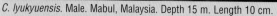

C. lyukyuensis. Sangihe Islands, Indonesia. **H** Depth 6 m. Length 55 mm. **I** Male. Depth 7 m. Length 9 cm.

Blue-scaled Fairy-wrasse *Cirrhilabrus cyanopleura*

Cheilinoides cyanopleura Bleeker, 1851. Java.

Andaman Sea to Bali. Abundant on Java's north coast, but uncommon in Bali where it has to compete with congeners. Its sibling *Cirrhilabrus lyukyuensis* ranges intermittently to Bali. *C. cyanopleura* occurs on coastal and inner reefs, sometimes forms large schools when feeding on zooplankton. Males are identified by the patch of scales with purple to blue margins in the centre of the body and none below the level of the pectoral fin base. Length to 11 cm.

C. cyanopleura. Pulau Putri, Java. Depth 6 m. Length 11 cm.

C. cyanopleura. Pulau Putri, Java. **B** Juveniles. Depth 6 m. Length 35 mm. **C** Male. Depth 6 m. Length 11 cm.

Fine-spotted Fairy-wrasse *Cirrhilabrus punctatus*

Cirrhilabrus punctatus Randall & Kuiter, 1989. GBR.

Known from eastern New Guinea, Solomon Islands and eastern Australia, ranging south to Montague Island as expatriates. Adults brown to blackish green-blue on sides and pale ventrally. Small blue ocellated spots scattered over the body that extend onto the median fins. Males change to various colours during courtship. Usually occurs in small aggregations to about 20 m deep. Length to 11 cm.

C. punctatus. Male. From Moreton Bay, Qld. Length 10 cm.

C. punctatus. Nuptial males. **B** GBR. Phil Woodhead. **C** Milne Bay, PNG. D. 20 m. Length 11 cm.

C. punctatus. **D** Juvenile. Montague Island, NSW. D. 10 m. Length 30 mm. **E** Female. GBR. Length about 75 mm. Phil Woodhead.

Cirrhilabrus randalli Allen, 1995. Rowley Shoals, WA.

A geographical variant of *Cirrhilabrus cyanopleura*, only known from the Rowley Shoals and Scott & Hibernia Reefs, off north-western Australia. A schooling species in lagoons and outer reefs to about 40 m depth. Part of the *cyanopleura*-complex, males distinguished by the broad yellow band on sides. The yellow lateral stripe has developed similarly to the yellow blotch in *C. lyukyuensis*, a sibling species. When schooling above the substrate to feed, the yellow mark seems to serve as a means of easy recognition so the fish can stay in touch with each other, and is more developed in oceanic areas. Length to 10 cm.

A

C. randalli. Nuptial male. Rowley Shoals. Depth 10 m. Length 10 cm.

B

C

C. randalli. Rowley Shoals, WA. **B** Depth 25 m. Length 75 mm. **C** Juvenile. Depth 8 m. Length 35 mm.

A

C. luteovittatus. Male. Aquarium. Length 10 cm. Scott Michael.

Yellow-band Fairy-wrasse *Cirrhilabrus luteovittatus*

Cirrhilabrus luteovittatus Randall, 1988. Marshall Is.

Known from the eastern islands and atolls of Micronesia. A close relative of *Cirrhilabrus solorensis* with their juveniles being virtually identical. Males have a broad yellowish mid-lateral band running from behind the pectoral fin to the caudal fin base. Occurs in small groups along reef margins over rubble substrates to about 25 m depth. Length to 10 cm.

B

C

C. luteovittatus. Males. Marshall Islands. Depth 12–20 m. Lengths about 10 cm. **B** Rob Myers. **C** Satoshi Yoshii.

Red-eyed Fairy-wrasse *Cirrhilabrus solorensis*

Cirrhilabrus solorensis Bleeker, 1853. Solor I.

Restricted region from the Flores and Banda Seas to north-eastern Sulawesi and west to Bali and Christmas Island in the Indian Ocean. Coastal to outer reef lagoons on rubble and coral habitats. Highly variable. Nuptial colour (**A**) can change from normal colour (**B**) in seconds. Usually nuptial colours are displayed during spawning, but in Sulawesi it is almost permanent, probably because of other *Cirrhilabrus* species there. The eye is bright red and males usually show a dark shading or band along the end of the gill cover. Length to 11 cm.

C. solorensis. Male variations. Flores. Depth 10 m. Length 10 cm.

C. solorensis. Flores. D. 10 m. L. 45 mm.

C. solorensis. Large females. Gilimanuk, Bali. D. 6 m. Length 10 cm.

Orange-back Wrasse *Cirrhilabrus aurantidorsalis*

Cirrhilabrus aurantidorsalis Allen & Kuiter, 1999.
Togean Islands, Tomini Bay, Sulawesi.

Only known from eastern Tomini Bay, Sulawesi. Occurs in small groups along reef edges with rubble patches in depths to about 25 m. Recognised by the yellow to orange back in all but very small juveniles. Males are more orange and have a dark red crown-like mark on the head. Length to 9 cm.

C. aurantidorsalis. **A** Juvenile. Depth 8 m. Length 40 mm. **B** Male. Depth 15 m. Length 10 cm. Tomini Bay, Sulawesi, Indonesia.

Katherine's Fairy-wrasse *Cirrhilabrus katherinae*

Cirrhilabrus katherinae Randall, 1992. Miyakejima, Japan.

Only known from Izu Islands, Japan, and the Mariana Islands. Occurs in small groups on rubble and algae reefs to about 40 m depth. Males with dusky to red band on sides. Females with yellow dorsal-fin base. Length to 80 mm.

C. katherinae. Males, **B** nuptial colours. Micronesia. Depth 18 m. Length 8 cm. Rob Myers.

C. katherinae. **C** Male. Kumejima, Japan. Length 75 mm. Tsuyoshi Kawamoto. **D** Juveniles and female. Guam. Depth 10 m.

C. rubripinnis. Philippines. Roger Steene.

Red-finned Fairy-wrasse *Cirrhilabrus rubripinnis*

Cirrhilabrus rubripinnis Randall & Carpenter, 1980. Philippines.

Philippines to northern Indonesia. Lives on open hard substrate with short algae and sparse coral or sponge growth at 30–40 m depth. Occurs in small groups, each with a single dominating male. Males have large dorsal and anal fins that are bright red and erected during display. It has red ventral fins with extremely long filaments. Length to 9 cm.

C. rubripinnis. Juvenile. Sulawesi. Scott Michael.

C. rubripinnis. Derawan, Kalimantan. Depth 40 m. Length 85 mm.

Girdled Fairy-wrasse *Cirrhilabrus balteatus*

Cirrhilabrus balteatus Randall, 1988. Marshall Islands.

Only known from Marshall Island region. This species schools on sparse reef and rubble sea beds, feeding up from the bottom on zooplankton, to a depth of about 20 m. Males are distinct from other sympatric species in the genus by their colour pattern and extremely long ventral fins, but females are difficult to distinguish as are most other members. Length to 10 cm.

C. balteatus. Marshall Islands. Depth 12 m. L. 85 mm. Satoshi Yoshii.

Conde's Fairy-wrasse *Cirrhilabrus condei*

Cirrhilabrus condei Allen & Randall, 1996. Madang, PNG.

Eastern New Guinea to northern Great Barrier Reef. Occurs in groups on sheltered shallow rubble-algae flats, usually at a few metres depth. Males display in an unusual way, erecting only the front two thirds of the dorsal fin (**C**). Males are distinct in having a black margin on the dorsal fin and a white line along the base of the fin. A small species, largest seen about 8 cm.

A

C. condei. Male. Milne Bay, PNG. D. 7 m. L. 65 mm. Jerry Allen.

B

C

D

E

C. condei. Milne Bay, PNG. D. 4 m. **B** Young male, **C** & **D** males, **D** nuptial. Length about 65 mm. **E** Female and male.

29

Lubbock's Fairy-wrasse *Cirrhilabrus lubbocki*

Cirrhilabrus lubbocki Randall & Carpenter, 1980.
Philippines.

Philippines to Flores seas. Coastal and inner reefs with low, but rich coral and algae coverage. Usually occurs in moderately large groups at depths of about 20-25 m. Variable in colour from pinkish to bright red or purple, and dorsal fin often bright yellow in adults. Closely related to *C. flavidorsalis* and juveniles or females are identical. Length to 9 cm.

C. lubbocki. Males. Flores, Indonesia. Depth 20 m. Length 75 mm.

C. lubbocki. Females. Flores. Depth 20 m. Length 65 mm.

C. lubbocki. Male. Flores, Indonesia. Depth 25 m. Length 9 cm.

C. lubbocki. Sangihe Is. Depth 10 m. Length 75 mm.

Debelius' Fairy-wrasse *Cirrhilabrus adornatus*

Cirrhilabrus adornatus Randall & Kunzmann, 1998.
Pulau Ular, off Padang, west coast Sumatra.

Only known from the islands off the west coast of Sumatra. It is closely related to *Cirrhilabrus flavidorsalis* and females are virtually identical. Some males of *C. flavidorsalis* have a nearly all white body, but head is more red. *C. adornatus* occurs on rubble flats, especially destroyed coral areas. It was first discovered by H. Debelius at the Mentawai Is. in 1997. Length to 65 mm.

C. adornatus. Mentawai Islands, West Sumatra, Indonesia. Depth 14 m. Length 65 mm. Helmut Debelius.

Yellow-fin Fairy-wrasse *Cirrhilabrus flavidorsalis*

Cirrhilabrus flavidorsalis Randall & Carpenter, 1980. Philippines.

Philippines to northern Indonesia and south to Flores seas. Occurs in sheltered bays on rubble slopes with a rich mix of coral, algae and sponges in shallow water where they form large groups such as in the Sangihe Islands in depths of less than 10 m, but seen to about 20 m. Males highly variable in colour with dorsal fin colours from all yellow to red or blue, and body from red to pink or white, depending on mood and stage. Length to 65 mm.

C. flavidorsalis. Indonesia. **A** Flores, male. D. 15 m. **B** & **C** Sangihe Islands. D. 6 m. **B** Females. L. 55 mm. **C** Male. L. 65 mm.

Walindi Fairy-wrasse *Cirrhilabrus walindi*

Cirrhilabrus walindi Allen & Randall, 1996. New Britain Id.

Eastern New Guinea and Solomon Islands. Occurs on rubble slopes with rich invertebrate growth. Usually seen in small groups of mostly females with males usually swimming loosely with them or higher above the substrate. Reported as shallow as 10 m at Kimbe Bay, but occurs mostly at 40–50 m depth and some males were observed high above the sea bed in pursuit of zooplankton. Readily identified by the black blotches on their back and lunare tail. Length to about 8 cm.

C. walindi. Male. Milne Bay, PNG. Depth 45 m. Length 75 mm.

C. walindi. Kimbe B, PNG. D. 15 m. L. 48 mm. J. Allen.

C. walindi. Pair. Milne Bay, PNG. Depth 45 m. Length 75 mm.

Pink-margin Wrasse *Cirrhilabrus rubrimarginatus*

Cirrhilabrus rubrimarginatus Randall, 1992.
Ryukyu Islands, Japan.

West Pacific from southern Japan to Indonesia and PNG. Deep coastal to outer reef drop-offs and steep rubble slopes and flats. Juveniles solitary amongst large rubble, usually at 20-30 m depth. Adults in small loose aggregations at moderate depths, usually at 40 m or more around patch reefs or bommies on open flat substrates. Large males with red margins on fins that look dusky in deep water. Length to 11 cm.

A. *C. rubrimarginatus*. Flores, Indonesia. Depth 50 m. Length 11 cm.

B. *C. rubrimarginatus*. Kerama, Japan. D. 25 m. L. 35 mm.

C. *C. rubrimarginatus*. Bali, Indonesia. D. 55 m. L. 10 cm. T. Tonozuka.

D. *C. rubrimarginatus*. Bali, Indonesia. D. 35 m. L. 50 mm.

E. *C. rubrimarginatus*. Male. Fiji. D. 20 m. L. 8 cm. Scott Michael.

G. *C. rubrimarginatus*. Kochi, Japan. **G** Nuptial colours. D. 26 m. L. 8 cm. **F** L. 35 mm. **H** L. 40 mm. Tomonori Hirata.

Blue-margin Fairy-wrasse *Cirrhilabrus pylei*

Cirrhilabrus pylei Allen & Randall, 1996.
Papua New Guinea.

West Pacific from Bali and PNG. Appears to be restricted to very deep water. Shallowest seen is 55 m. Very similar to *Cirrhilabrus rubrimarginatus* but male has blue margin on caudal fin and even longer ventral fins. Both species co-occur at Menjangan I., Bali. Length to 9 cm.

C. pylei. Male. Depth 85 m. Length 75 mm. Akira Ogawa

C. pylei. Female. Aquarium, Scott Michael.

C. pylei. Menjangan I., Bali. Depth 55 m. L. 8 cm. Takamasa Tonozuka.

Rosy-fin Fairy-wrasse *Cirrhilabrus* sp 1

Undescribed species

Coral Sea region. Usually a deep water species, but according to Fenton Walsh at Holmes reef it occurs at depths as shallow as 6–8 m over rubble sea beds. A distinctly coloured species and the deep pink colouration of the dorsal fin is unique. Length to about 9 cm.

C. sp 1. From Holmes Reef, Qld, Australia. Depth 6–8 m. Fenton Walsh.

Lavender Fairy-wrasse *Cirrhilabrus lineatus*

Cirrhilabrus lineatus Randall & Lubbock, 1982.
New Caledonia.

Great Barrier Reef and Coral Sea. Appears to replace the closely related *Cirrhilabrus rubrimarginatus* in the rest of the West Pacific and records of latter south of PNG are probably based on *C. lineatus*. Occurs on deep slopes and along drop-offs at depths from 15 m, usually in about 30–50 m depth. Males easily identified by their distinctive colouration. Females pink with many blue lines on their head and body, with the central ones breaking into spots on the body. Length to 11 cm.

C. lineatus. Male. From Holmes Reef. L. 10 cm. Fenton Walsh.

C. lineatus. GBR. D. 25 m. **B** Female. L. 75 mm. **C** Juvenile. L. 35 mm. **B** Male. L. 11 cm. **B–D** Phil Woodhead.

Earle's Fairy-wrasse *Cirrhilabrus earlei*

Cirrhilabrus earlei Randall & Pyle, 2001. Palau.

Only known from Palau. A deep water species. Occurs on rubble slopes at the base of deep drop-offs, usually at depths of more than 50 m. The type specimens were collected at depths over 80 m. It has a distinct striped colour pattern and the adults have a pointed caudal fin that appears to become more truncate in males. Length to 85 mm.

C. earlei. Palau. Depth 50–60 m. **A** Female, **B** male, **C** small juvenile, and **D** large juvenile. **A–D** Hiroshi Nagano.

Diamond-tail Fairy-wrasse
Cirrhilabrus rhomboidalis

Cirrhilabrus rhomboidalis Randall, 1988. Marshall Is.

Only known from the Marshall Islands. Reported on sand and rubble slopes to 40 m depth. Stay lower to the substrate compared with other species of *Cirrhilabrus*. Largest known specimen, the male type, is 102 mm long.

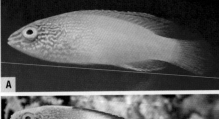

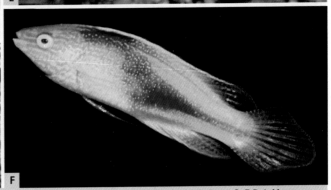

C. rhomboidalis. **A** Juvenile, **B** young male. Aquarium import from Marshall Islands. Yataka Niino.

C. rhomboidalis. Marshall Islands. Depth 20 m. **C** Juveniles. **D–F** Males, last 2 nuptial, lengths 6–8 cm. **C–F** Rob Myers.

Walsh's Fairy-wrasse *Cirrhilabrus walshi*

Cirrhilabrus walshi Randall & Pyle, 2000. Coral Sea.

Only known from Coral Sea to American Samoa, from a few specimens collected at depths of 37–46 m. It is similar to *Cirrhilabrus condei* but more slender and with a differently coloured dorsal fin. Length to about 75 mm.

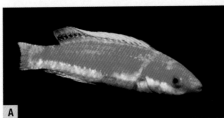

C. walshi. Specimens from Pago Pago. Fenton Walsh.

Tono's Fairy-wrasse *Cirrhilabrus tonozukai*

Cirrhilabrus tonozukai Allen & Kuiter, 1999. Sulawesi.

Eastern Sulawesi, Lembeh Strait to the Banggai Islands and Palau. It occurs on open, hard-bottom substrates with algae and sparse coral growth, usually in strong current zones. Juveniles and females in small groups, sometimes with several males of which the largest is dominant. Depth range 15-40 m. Juveniles and females similar to several other species and identification depends on the presence of a male that has a long dorsal filament and red anal fin, with the latter looking black in natural light. Length to 75 mm.

C. tonozukai. Males. Sulawesi. D. 35 m. L. 75 mm. **A** T. Tonozuka.

C. tonozukai. Male. Palau. Hiroshi Nagano.

C. tonozukai. Juvs & fems. Lembeh Strait. L. 35–60 mm.

Whip-fin Fairy-wrasse *Cirrhilabrus filamentosus*

Cirrhilabrichthys filamentosus Klausewitz, 1976. Java Sea.

Southern Indonesian waters, from Java and Timor seas. Occurs on deep muddy coastal slopes and is primarily known from deep water trawls, but it also lives in shallow muddy estuaries. Usually occurs in small groups of juveniles, females and a single dominating large male. Mixes with other species of *Cirrhilabrus* or with *Paracheilinus* to feed high above substrate on zooplankton. A spectacular species during display which can change from normal (**B**) to nuptial (**A**) in seconds, and back again. Length to 8 cm.

C. filamentosus. Bali, Indonesia. **A** Male. Depth 6 m. Length 8 cm. **B** Male. Depth 20 m. Length 8 cm. **C** Female. D. 6 m. L. 6 cm.

Social Fairy-wrasse *Cirrhilabrus rubriventralis*

Cirrhilabrus rubriventralis Springer & Randall, 1974. Red Sea.

Red Sea and western Indian Ocean. Replaced by similar *Cirrhilabrus joanallenae* in eastern Indian Ocean. Identified by the long dorsal-fin rays and long ventrals that are reddish. Length to 85 mm.

A

C. rubriventralis. Aquarium. Yutaka Niino.

B

C. rubriventralis. Red Sea specimen. Helmut Debelius.

Pulauweh Fairy-wrasse *Cirrhilabrus joanallenae*

Cirrhilabrus joanallenae Allen, 2000. Pulau Weh, Sumatra.

Only known from Sumatra, but probably ranges from Andaman Sea to Java Seas. Often exported from Bali in the aquarium trade. Closely related to *Cirrhilabrus rubriventralis* from the Red Sea and it is not clear if the species are actually geographical variations or if they overlap in range. Latter is doubtful, but a specimen in the aquarium trade received from Sri Lanka could be either species (**B**). The large males in both species have large dark ventral fins that are red in *C. rubriventralis* and black in *C. joanallenae*, but apart from colour there are slight differences in meristics such as pectoral fin count. Occurs on rubble slopes in 20-40 m depth. Length to 85 mm.

A

B

C. joanallenae? Female. Aquarium import from Sri Lanka that appears to be this species. Fenton Walsh.

C

C. joanallenae. Male. Pulau Weh, northern Sumatra. Depth 20 m. Length 8 cm. **A** Roger Steene. **C** Takamasa Tonozuka.

D

E

C. joanallenae? Aquarium imports from Indonesia (Java?) that may be this species. Scott Michael.

KwaZulu Fairy-wrasse *Cirrhilabrus* sp 2.
Undetermined species, appears to be undescribed.

Known from off South Africa and has been referred to as *Cirrhilabrus rubriventralis*, but is clearly different and shows some similarities to *C. morrisoni*, especially the female. Depth range given by Dennis King, who photographed this species, is 25–50 m. Length to 65 mm.

C. sp 2. KwaZulu-Natal. Depth 30 m. **A** Male. Length 65 mm. **B** Female. Length 50 mm. Dennis King.

Morrison's Fairy-wrasse *Cirrhilabrus morrisoni*
Cirrhilabrus morrisoni Hibernia Reef, off northern WA.

Known from Hibernia Reef in the western Timor Sea, off the Australian coast, about 130 km south of Roti I., Indonesia. Occurs on open substrates with rubble and dense *Halimeda* algae growth at about 30 m depth. Males are distinctive with their black fins. A small species, length to 55 mm.

C. morrisoni. Hibernia Reef, nw Australia. Depth 30 m. **A** Male. Length 55 mm. Jerry Allen. **B** Juvenile. Length 50 mm. Clay Bryce.

Rosy-scales Fairy-wrasse *Cirrhilabrus rubrisquamis*
Cirrhilabrus rubrisquamis Randall & Emery, 1983.
Chagos Archipelago.

Only known from the Maldives. Chagos Archipelago and Sri Lanka regions. Mainly found along deep drop-offs to about 50 m depth. Occurs in invertebrate rich habitats, sometimes in small groups below reef overhangs. Scales on front part of body have dark edges when adult. During courting displays the male turns almost white on its sides with any red colouring mostly confined to the head area. A small species, length to 65 mm.

C. rubrisquamis. Aquarium photographs. **A** Young male. Hiroyuki Tanaka. **B** Male and **C** female. Scott Michael.

Blood-stain Fairy-wrasse *Cirrhilabrus sanguineus*

Cirrhilabrus sanguineus Cornic, 1987. Mauritius.

Only known from Mauritius. A deep water species found on rubble slopes away from drop-offs at 40–60 m depth. Males are readily identified by the red bar midway along the body that looks black in deep water. Length to 65 mm.

A
C. sanguineus. Mauritius. Depth 60 m. Hugues Vitry.

B
C. sanguineus. Neotype, 91 mm. Aquarium, Mauritius. Roger Steene.

Kato's Fairy-wrasse *Cirrhilabrus katoi*

Cirrhilabrus katoi Senou & Hirata, 2000. Izu Is., Japan.

Only known from islands off the Izu Peninsula and south to Kashiwajima. Occurs in groups over rocky substrates, commonly mixing with congeners to about 40 m depth. Small groups usually comprise females with one or two males. Length to about 10 cm.

A

B
C. katoi. Kochi, Japan. D. 20 m. L. 20 mm. T. Hirata.

C
C. katoi. Kochi, Japan. D. 24 m. L. 35 mm. T. Hirata.

D
C. katoi. Nuptial males. Kochi, Japan. D. 27 m. L. 10 cm. Tomonori Hirata.

E
C. katoi. Kochi, Japan. D. 24 m. L. 7 cm. T. Hirata.

F
C. katoi. Male. Kochi, Japan. D. 25 m. L. 80 mm. Tomonori Hirata.

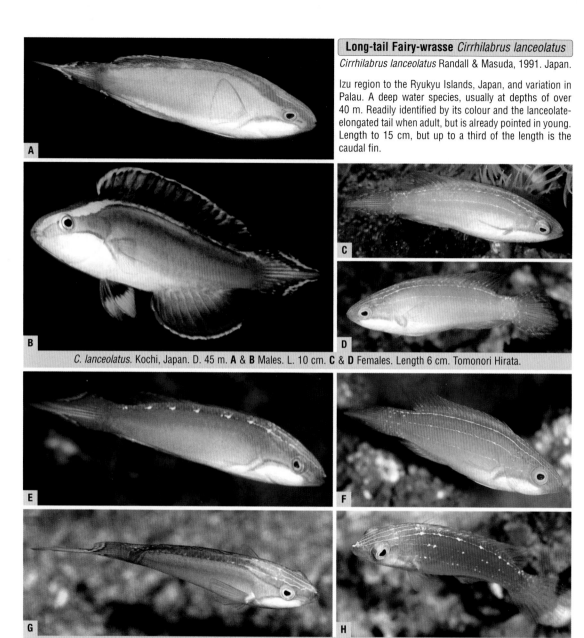

Cirrhilabrus lanceolatus Randall & Masuda, 1991. Japan.

Izu region to the Ryukyu Islands, Japan, and variation in Palau. A deep water species, usually at depths of over 40 m. Readily identified by its colour and the lanceolate-elongated tail when adult, but is already pointed in young. Length to 15 cm, but up to a third of the length is the caudal fin.

C. lanceolatus. Kochi, Japan. D. 45 m. **A** & **B** Males. L. 10 cm. **C** & **D** Females. Length 6 cm. Tomonori Hirata.

C. lanceolatus. Kumejima, Japan. **F** & **G** Male. L. 14 cm. **F** & **H** Juveniles. L. 50 & 45 mm. **E**–**H** Tsuyoshi Kawamoto.

C. lanceolatus. Male. Palau. Length 9 cm. Hiroshi Nagano.

Splendid Fairy-wrasse
Cirrhilabrus cf *lanceolatus*

Izu region to the Ryukyu Islands, Japan. A deep water species, males beautifully adorned with multiple colours during courtship display (**A**). A currently undescribed species that was confused with *Cirrhilabrus lanceolatus* because of the similar caudal fin shape. Length to 12 cm.

A
C. cf *lanceolatus.* Kochi, Japan. L. 12 cm. D. 38 m. Tomonori Hirata.

C
C. cf *lanceolatus.* Kochi. L. 6 cm. D. 40 m. T. Hirata.

D
C. cf *lanceolatus.* Kochi. L. 4 cm. D. 30 m. T. Hirata.

B
C. cf *lanceolatus.* Kumejima, Japan. Tsuyoshi Kawamoto.

E
C. cf *lanceolatus.* Kochi. L. 7 cm. D. 38 m. T. Hirata.

F
C. cf *lanceolatus.* Kochi, Japan. L. 8 cm. D. 38 m. Tomonori Hirata.

G
C. cf *lanceolatus.* Kochi. L. 5 cm. D. 42 m. T. Hirata.

H
C. cf *lanceolatus.* Kochi, Japan, L. 6 cm. D. 36 m. Tomonori Hirata.

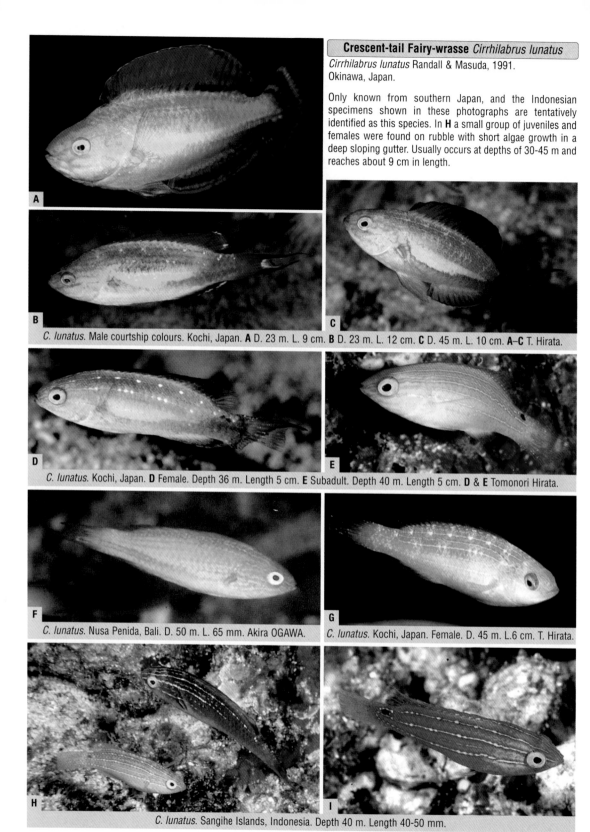

Crescent-tail Fairy-wrasse *Cirrhilabrus lunatus*

Cirrhilabrus lunatus Randall & Masuda, 1991.
Okinawa, Japan.

Only known from southern Japan, and the Indonesian specimens shown in these photographs are tentatively identified as this species. In **H** a small group of juveniles and females were found on rubble with short algae growth in a deep sloping gutter. Usually occurs at depths of 30-45 m and reaches about 9 cm in length.

C. lunatus. Male courtship colours. Kochi, Japan. **A** D. 23 m. L. 9 cm. **B** D. 23 m. L. 12 cm. **C** D. 45 m. L. 10 cm. **A–C** T. Hirata.

C. lunatus. Kochi, Japan. **D** Female. Depth 36 m. Length 5 cm. **E** Subadult. Depth 40 m. Length 5 cm. **D & E** Tomonori Hirata.

C. lunatus. Nusa Penida, Bali. D. 50 m. L. 65 mm. Akira OGAWA.   *C. lunatus*. Kochi, Japan. Female. D. 45 m. L.6 cm. T. Hirata.

C. lunatus. Sangihe Islands, Indonesia. Depth 40 m. Length 40-50 mm.

Labout's Fairy-wrasse *Cirrhilabrus laboutei*

Cirrhilabrus laboutei Randall & Lubbock, 1982.
New Caledonia.

Great Barrier Reef and New Caledonia. Occurs mainly on outer reefs, from the upper slopes in rubble gutters to rubble zones below drop-offs to at least 50 m depth. Usually in small groups. Has a distinctive colouration and changes little with growth or between sexes. Length to 75 mm.

A

C. laboutei. Male. Great Barrier Reef. L. 85 mm. Fenton Walsh.

B

C. laboutei. Juvenile. GBR. L. 30 mm. Phil Woodhead.

C

C. laboutei. Female. GBR. L. 65 mm. Roger Steene

Red Sea Fairy-wrasse *Cirrhilabrus blatteus*

Cirrhilabrus blatteus Springer & Randall, 1974. Red Sea.

A Red Sea endemic. Occurs in small groups of females and a single male, usually on deep rubble slopes along reef margins. Identified by its long tail with yellow, and purple body-lines. Length to 10 cm.

A

C. blatteus. Female. Red Sea. Thomas Paulus.

B

C. blatteus. Male. Red Sea. Helmut Debelius.

Flame Fairy-wrasse *Cirrhilabrus jordani*

Cirrhilabrus jordani Snyder, 1904. Hawaiian Is.

Hawaiian endemic. Occurs in groups of mostly females, usually at depths of more than 20 m. Easily identified by its distinctive colouration. Length to 10 cm.

A

B

C. jordani. **A** Male. **B** Juvenile or female. Aquarium imports. **A** & **B** Yutaka Niino.

Black-fin Fairy-wrasse *Cirrhilabrus melanomarginatus*

Cirrhilabrus melanomarginatus Randall & Shen, 1989. Taiwan.

South China Sea, Philippines to southern Japan. Clear ocean reefs at various depths to about 40 m. Adults identified by the black outer margin of the dorsal fin and their large size when fully grown. A large species that can reach 15 cm.

C. melanomarginatus. Japan. **A & B** Nuptial males. Okinawa. **A** T. Kawamoto. **B** K. Yunokawa. **C** Kochi. D. 8 m. L. 6 cm. T. Hirata.

Scott's Fairy-wrasse *Cirrhilabrus scottorum*

Cirrhilabrus scottorum Randall & Pyle, 1989. Tahiti.

South Pacific, Great Barrier Reef to Pitcairn Group, but some geographical variations may represent separate species. Occurs in lagoons and outer reef habitats. Usually in small groups of females with fewer males when feeding above the sea bed on zooplankton. Juveniles on rubble substrates which stay close to the sea bed. Males are readily identified by their distinctive colours. Length to 10 cm.

C. scottorum. GBR, Australia. **A & B** Males, length 10 cm, depths: **A** 24 m, **B** 6 m. **C** Juveniles about 45 mm. **A–C** Phil Woodhead.

C. scottorum. Aquarium photos. **D** from Holmes Reef, Qld, Australia. L. 10 cm. **E** from Samoa. **D & E** Fenton Walsh.

C. scottorum. Aquarium photos. **F** Origin unknown. **E** from Tonga. **F & G** Scott Michael.

Exquisite Wrasse *Cirrhilabrus exquisitus*

Cirrhilabrus exquisitus Smith, 1957. Mozambique.

Widespread Indian Ocean, ranging east to Sumatra. Occurs on reef edges and around bommies with rubble zones. Usually in moderately large, mixed sex groups whilst feeding on zooplankton, often high above the substrate. Males often display to each other. To about 40 m depth. Length to 11 cm.

A

B

C

C. exquisitus. Males, **A** & **B** nuptial, **C** non-excited. Maldives. Depth about 30 m. Length 10–11 cm.

Pacific Exquisite Wrasse *Cirrhilabrus* cf *exquisites*

West Pacific from Philippines to Indonesia and Australia to Fiji, but distinct geographical variations in Western Australia, Japan and Fiji. Occurs on shallow outer reef crests, or upper edge of drop-offs. Males display by swimming quickly along with fins erect and intensified bright colours. Length to 10 cm.

B

A

C

C. cf *exquisites.* Nuptial males (var-1) Indonesia. **A** Flores. D. 6 m. L. 10 cm. **B** Sangihe Is. D. 4 m. L. 85 mm. **C** as **B** non-excited.

D

E

C. cf *exquisites.* Nuptial male (var-2). **D** Fiji. Gary Bell. **E** (var-3). Kochi, Japan. Depth 18 m. Length 8 cm. Tomonori Hirata.

F

G

C. cf *exquisites.* Males, **G** nuptial (var-4). Rowley Shoals, Western Australia. Depth 16 m. Length 75 mm.

GENUS *Conniella* Allen, 1983

Feminine. Type species: *Coniella apterygia* Allen, by original designation. A monotypic genus that appears to most closely related to the genus *Cirrhilabrus*. *Coniella* lacks ventral fins, but in terms of body colour patterns, fins and behaviour it is just like *Cirrhilabrus*. Usually swims low over rubble slopes, but rises to feed on zooplanton, often swimming with anthiids. Aquarium details are not known but are likely to be the same as for *Cirrhilabrus*.

Rowley Shoals Wrasse *Conniella apterygia*

Coniella apterygia Allen, 1983. Rowley Shoals.

Only known from the Rowley Shoals and Scott Reef, off the north-western Australian coast. Occurs in small to large groups, primarily on deep rubble slopes that are below the outer reef walls in depths from 35 to 50 m, but also found in lagoons as shallow as 12 m (**C & D**). Readily identified by their colouration with no similar species in the same area. Juveniles have a rounded tail and a small black spot on the caudal peduncle, features found in many small *Cirrhilabrus*. Length to about 9 cm, but usually much smaller. Large individuals occur in small groups and all appear to be male.

C. apterygia. All photographs: Rowley Shoals, WA. **A** Large male, about 9 cm. **B** Various angles, showing the lack of ventral fins. **C** Juvenile, about 35 mm. **D** Male, about 65 mm. **E** Swimming with anthiids (undescribed species), a mixture that is a common occurrence on deep slopes when feeding on zooplankton that are carried by the currents. **F** A male with a probable female below.

GENUS *Pseudocheilinus* Bleeker, 1962

Masculine. Type species: *Cheilinus hexataenia* Bleeker, 1857. A small genus comprising 7 Indo-Pacific species.

1 *Pseudocheilinus citrinus* Randall, 1999 **Citrus Pitcairn Wrasse**
2 *Pseudocheilinus dispilus* Randall, 1999 **Two-spot Réunion Wrasse**
3 *Pseudocheilinus evanidus* Jordan & Evermann, 1903 **Pin-striped Wrasse** (p. 48)
4 *Pseudocheilinus hexataenia* (Bleeker, 1857) **Six-line Wrasse** (this page)
5 *Pseudocheilinus ocellatus* Randall, 1999 **White-barred Pink Wrasse** (p. 48)
6 *Pseudocheilinus octotaenia* Jenkins, 1901 **Eight-line Wrasse** (p. 49)
7 *Pseudocheilinus tetrataenia* Schultz, 1960 **Four-line Wrasse**

Remarks
All members are small and colourful fishes, usually occurring secretively in rock or coral reefs. Most species occur in small but loose aggregations that may be spread over a small section of reef. They feed on the substrate on small invertebrates but also take zooplankton that drift close to the sea bed. Unlike many wrasses, the various stages from juvenile to adult are very similar in terms of colour.

All the species are easily kept in captivity and ideally suited to the invertebrate aquarium.

Six-line Wrasse *Pseudocheilinus hexataenia*
Cheilinus hexataenia Bleeker, 1857. Ambon.

Widespread Indo-West Pacific. Clear coastal to outer reefs. In dense coral habitats on shallow reef crests or slopes to a depth of about 20 m. Usually occurs in small loose groups. A shy species, usually swimming amongst the protection of coral branches. Identified by the brightly colour lined pattern and the small ocellus on the caudal fin base. Length to 85 mm.

A

P. hexataenia. Bali, Indonesia. Depth 8 m. Length 75 mm.

B

P. hexataenia. Mabul. D. 8 m. L. 55 mm.

C

P. hexataenia. Bali, Indonesia. Depth 15 m. Length 85 mm.

Pseudocheilinus ocellatus Randall, 1999.
Marshall Islands.

Widespread West to Central Pacific. Mainly found in oceanic locations on clear coastal to outer reef slopes and walls. Usually in caves or crevices with rich invertebrate growth to at least 40 m depth. Identified by the false eye-spot on the caudal peduncle and usually with thin white bars on the body. Length to 12 cm.

P. ocellatus. Great Barrier Reef, Australia. Depth 25 m. **A** Length 55 mm. **B** Length 85 mm. **C** Length 45 mm. **A–C** Phil Woodhead.

Pin-striped Wrasse
Pseudocheilinus evanidus

Pseudocheilinus evanidus Jenkins, 1901.
Hawaiian Islands.

Widespread Indo-West Pacific. Clear coastal to outer reef slopes and walls with rich invertebrate growth. Usually in caves or crevices to at least 40 m depth. Identified by the numerous thin longitudinal lines along the body. Length to 8 cm.

P. evanidus. **A** & **B** Bali, Indonesia. Depth 15 m. Length 65 mm.

P. evanidus. Maldives. Depth 25 m. Length 55 mm.

P. evanidus. Flores. Depth 7 m. Length 45 mm.

Eight-line Wrasse
Pseudocheilinus octotaenia

Pseudocheilinus octotaenia Jenkins, 1901.
Hawaiian Islands.

Widespread Indo-West Pacific. Clear coastal to outer reef slopes and walls. Usually in caves or crevices with rich invertebrate growth to at least 40 m depth. Identified by the eight longitudinal lines along the body. Length to 12 cm.

A

P. octotaenia. Kalimantan, Indonesia. Depth 30 m. Length 12 cm.

B
P. octotaenia. Flores. D. 25 m. L. 11 cm.

C
P. octotaenia. Bali, Indonesia. Depth 15 m. Length 12 cm.

GENUS *Pseudocheilinops* Schultz, 1960

Masculine. Type species: *Pseudocheilinops ataenia* Schultz, by original designation. A monotypic genus similar to *Pseudocheilinus*. Highly secretive in rich habitats of mixed coral and algae on sheltered deep slopes. Well suited to the invertebrate aquarium and feeds by picking tiny creatures from the substrate.

Pink-streaked Wrasse *Pseudocheilinops ataenia*

Pseudocheilinops ataenia Schultz, 1960. Sulawesi.

Indonesia to Philippines and Palau. Occurs in dense coral and algae growth on reef slopes at 20 m+. Mainly in still coastal waters where brittle corals grow high. In small groups feeding actively amongst dead parts of corals with coralline algae, seeking out small crustacea. Easily overlooked because of small size. Length to 65 mm, but usually much smaller.

A

B

C

P. ataenia. Maumere, Flores. Depth 25 m. Length 45 cm. **A** & **C** Male. **B** Female.

GENUS *Wetmorella* Fowler & Bean, 1928

Feminine. Type species: *Wetmorella philippina* Fowler & Bean, 1928. A small genus comprising 3 Indo-Pacific species.

1 *Wetmorella albofasciata* Schultz & Marshall, 1954 **White-banded Possum-wrasse**
2 *Wetmorella nigropinnata* (Seale, 1901) **Yellow-banded Possum-wrasse**
3 *Wetmorella triocellata* Schultz & Marshall, 1954 **Pygmy Possum-wrasse**

Remarks

This genus comprises a few but interesting species that typically live in the back and dark parts of caves. Usually found along outer reef walls at moderate depths, but occasionally in sheltered lagoons.

All the species are easily kept in captivity and are ideally suited to the invertebrate aquarium. They are extremely shy and should be kept with other small fishes that are not aggressive or too competitive for food. Species that also graze on tiny prey from the substrate, such as mandarinfish (Callionymidae), are good companions.

A

Yellow-banded Possum-wrasse
Wetmorella nigropinnata

Cheilinus nigropinnatus Seale, 1901. Guam.

Widespread Indo-West Pacific. Secretive in large dark caves along steep slopes and drop-offs from deep coastal lagoons to outer reef walls. Usually occur in small groups, but easily missed unless specifically looking for them. Juveniles yellowish green to brown with thick vertical white lines. Males reddish-brown with yellow lines. Length to 65 mm.

W. nigropinnata. Maldives. Depth 25 m. Length 45 mm.

B

W. nigropinnata. Flores, Indonesia. Depth 30 m. Length 55 mm.

C

W. nigropinnata. Sipadan. Depth 30 m. Length 20 mm.

D

W. nigropinnata. Flores, Indonesia. D. 20 m. L. 40 mm.

E

W. nigropinnata. Maldives. D. 15 m. L. 40 mm.

White-banded Possum-wrasse
Wetmorella albofasciata

Wetmorella albofasciata Schultz & Marshall, 1954.
Philippines.

Widespread Indo-West Pacific. Coastal to outer reef slopes and drop-offs at the back of invertebrate rich caves. Usually in depths over 20 m, but occasionally shallow in lagoons or sheltered bays when suitable habitat available. Length to 55 mm.

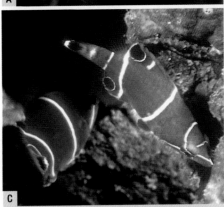

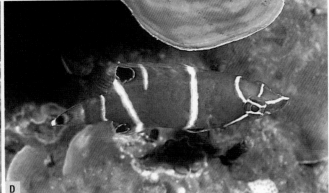

W. albofasciata. **A** & **C** Maldives.
Depth 25 m. Length. 35 mm.

W. albofasciata. **B** & **D** Tomini Bay, Sulawesi. **B** Depth 20 m.
Length 45 mm. **D** Depth 25 m. Length 35 mm.

Pygmy Possum-wrasse
Wetmorella triocellata

Wetmorella triocellata Schultz & Marshall, 1954.
Philippines.

Known from a few specimens. Differs from similar *Wetmorella albofasciata* in having a straight vertical line in front of the ocelli and anal-fin ocellus elongated. Secretive in coral and algae rubble on coastal or inner reef slopes in about 30 m depth. Length to 50 mm.

W. triocellata. Flores. From 30 m. L. 45 mm.

W. triocellata. Aquarium import from Philippines. Yutaka Niino.

GENUS *Epibulus* Cuvier, 1815

Masculine. Type species: *Sparus insidiator* Pallas, 1770. A monotypic Indo-Pacific genus, closely related to *Cheilinus*. Characterised by its extremely protractile mouth and long jaws. Several geographical variations.

Remarks

This genus comprises a single but unusual species in which the mouth is expanded forwards to form a tube for strong suction and has a long lower jaw to capture prey. Adults are highly variable in colour and some individuals may be bright yellow. Small juveniles resemble possum wrasses *(Wetmorella* spp). Easily maintained in an aquarium but should be kept with other fishes of similar size. Small individuals are suitable for the invertebrate aquarium, but will have to be moved when they grow larger and may turn on shrimps or small fishes.

A

E. insidiator. Fully coloured male. Qld, Australia. Depth 15 m. Length 25 cm.

Slingjaw Wrasse *Epibulus insidiator*

Sparus insidiator Pallas 1770. Java.

Widespread Indo-West Pacific. Coastal to outer reef habitats. Adults usually along deep slopes or drop-offs. Colour varies with age and sex, and a xanthic form. The various geographical forms appear to represent a single species, including in the Red Sea. Best recognised by its unusual mouth that extends to the end of the head in its closed position. The jaws swing forward into a long tube to create a strong suction to catch prey, taking in crustaceans and small fishes. Sometimes the Slingjaw Wrasse visits cleaning stations, holding its mouth fully extended and open for inspection. Length to 25 cm.

B

E. insidiator. Male. Rowley Shoals, WA. Depth 8 m. Length 23 cm.

C

D

E. insidiator. Males. Maldives. Depth 10–15 m. Length 22–25 cm.

E

F

E. insidiator. **E** Female. Flores, Indonesia. D. 10 m. L. 15 cm. **F** Female with *Labroides dimidiatus.* Maldives. D. 10 m. L. 14 cm.

E. insidiator. Flores, Indonesia. **G** Juvenile. Depth 15 m. Length 30 mm. **H** Female. Depth 15 m. Length 22 cm.

E. insidiator. Xanthic form. Tulamben, Bali. Depth 14 m. Length 20 cm. **I** Small *Labroides* cleaner wrasse checking the gills.

E. insidiator. Xanthic form with black pectoral fins. Milne Bay, PNG. Depth 12 m. Length 20 cm.

E. insidiator. Xanthic forms. **M** Qld, Australia. D. 8 m. L. 20 cm. **N** Egypt, Red Sea. D. 10 m. L. 20 cm.

Masculine. Type species: *Cossyphus opercularis* Peters, 1855 (= *Pteragogus pelycus* Randall, 1981). A small Indo-Pacific genus comprising about 10 species, several of which appear to be undescribed.

1 *Pteragogus aurigarius* (Richardson, 1845) **Malachite Wrasse** (p. 58)
2 *Pteragogus cryptus* Randall, 1981 **Red Sea Sneaky-wrasse** (p. 55)
3 *Pteragogus* cf *cryptus* 1 **Pacific Sneaky-wrasse** (p. 56)
4 *Pteragogus* cf *cryptus* 2 **Indian Sneaky-wrasse** (p. 56)
5 *Pteragogus enneacanthus* (Bleeker, 1853) **Cockerel Wrasse** (p. 57)
6 *Pteragogus flagellifer* (Valenciennes, 1839) **Cocktail Wrasse** (p. 55)
7 *Pteragogus guttatus* (Fowler & Bean, 1928) **White-barred Sneaky-wrasse** (p. 58)
8 *Pteragogus pelycus* Randall, 1981 **Seagrass Sneaky-wrasse** (this page)
9 *Pteragogus taeniops* (Peters, 1855) **Cheek-bar Sneaky-wrasse** (p. 57)
10 *Pteragogus* sp 1 (Red Bar) **Lembeh Sneaky-wrasse** (p. 55)

Remarks

Most members of this genus are extremely shy and secretive. They are well camouflaged in their habitat and are capable of quick colour changes. Few species are sexually dimorphic with males more colourful or with filamentous extensions on certain fin-spines. Divers occasionally observe them swimming in the open from one hide-out to another or when moving through soft-corals or algae. Few species were kept in aquariums but those that were, readily adapted to captivity. Small individuals do well in the invertebrate aquarium. They are extremely shy at first but soon learn who feeds them and become very tame.

P. pelycus. Mauritius. Depth 20 m. Length 10 cm. Jerry Allen.

Seagrass Sneaky-wrasse *Pteragogus pelycus*

Cossyphus opercularis Peters, 1855. Mozambique. = preoccupied.
Pteragogus pelycus Randall, 1981. Replacement name.

Western Indian Ocean and Red Sea, but latter appears to be a different species that is undescribed. Sheltered bays, mainly amongst seagrass or reefs with thick algae growth to about 20 m depth. Occurs in small loose aggregations and most hide. Occasionally one can be seen above the seagrass bed checking out its surroundings. Identified by the false eye mark on the end of the gill-plate. Length to 15 cm.

P. cf *pelycus*. Egypt, Red Sea. Depth 5 m. Length 12–15 cm.

Cocktail Wrasse *Pteragogus flagellifer*

Ctenolabrus flagellifer Valenciennes, 1839. No locality.

Widespread Indo-Pacific. Common in sheltered shallow bays with mixed rubble and dense algae growth, especially with mixed *Sargassum*, and seagrasses. Usually at a few metres depth, moving about amongst the weeds. Colour varies from green to light brown, matching habitat and adults have filamentous dorsal and anal fin rays. Length to 14 cm.

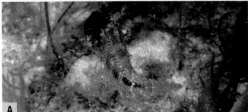

A

B

P. flagellifer. WA. **A** Female. Monte Bellos. Depth 3 m. Length 9 cm. **B** Male. Pt. Gregory. Depth 4 m. Length 14 cm. Barry Hutchins.

Lembeh Sneaky-wrasse *Pteragogus* sp 1

Undetermined species.

Only known eastern to northern Sulawesi. In Lembeh Strait the habitat consisted of a large area of various invertebrates growing low on rubble in a sheltered bay with muddy slopes. Adult deep bodied with a distinct red bar below the eye. This species has 10 dorsal spines, but lacks the elongated dorsal fin spines of other 10-spined species and has a red-edged ocellus surrounded by yellow on the gill cover. Length to about 8 cm.

A

P. sp 1. Sulawesi, Indonesia. Depth 24 m. Length 8 cm.

B

P. sp 1. Sulawesi, Indonesia. Depth 8 m. Length 35 mm.

C

P. sp 1. Sulawesi, Indonesia. Depth 8 m. Length 55 mm.

Red Sea Sneaky-wrasse *Pteragogus cryptus*

Pteragogus cryptus Randall, 1981. Red Sea.

Reported as widespread Indo-Pacific, but true species may be restricted to the Red Sea. Sheltered inner reefs and estuaries with large soft coral colonies or algae beds. It has 10 dorsal spines, lacks distinct vertical barring or longitudinal lines, and has yellow or white-edged ocellus on the gill cover that elongates in large individuals. First 3 dorsal fin spines elongated in adults. Length to about 85 mm.

P. cryptus. Egypt, Red Sea. Depth 5 m. Length 8 cm.

A

P. cf *cryptus* 1. Sangihe Is., Indonesia. D. 12 m. L. 9 cm.

Pacific Sneaky-wrasse *Pteragogus* cf *cryptus* 1

Widespread West Pacific, ranging west to Bali. Sheltered coastal to outer reef habitats in rich coral slopes, usually with soft corals. It has 10 dorsal spines and lacks distinct vertical barring or longitudinal lines but usually has a distinct white line from the tip of the snout, running over the top of the eye to the end of the gill cover. A yellow or pink edged ocellus on gill cover that reduces in size or fades in large individuals. First 3 dorsal fin spines elongated in adults. Length to about 9 cm.

B

P. cf *cryptus* 1. Bali, Indonesia. Depth 7 m. Length 8 cm.

C

P. cf *cryptus* 1. Flores, Indonesia. D. 8 m. L. 75 mm.

A

Indian Sneaky-wrasse *Pteragogus* cf *cryptus* 2

Widespread Indian Ocean, ranging west to Bali. Sheltered coastal to outer reef habitats on rich coral slopes, usually amongst staghorn coral rubble with algae. It has 10 dorsal spines and most scales have pale edges. It has a distinct white line running from the tip of the snout, over the top of the eye to the end of the gill cover and continuing over most of the body. A prominent pale, yellow-edged ocellus on the gill-cover. First 3 dorsal fin spines elongated in adults. Length to about 65 cm.

C

P. cf *cryptus* 2. **A** & **C** Pulau Putri. Depth 10 m. Length 65 mm.

B

P. cf *cryptus* 2. Rowley Shoals, WA. D. 10 m. L. 65 mm.

Cockerel Wrasse *Pteragogus enneacanthus*
Crenilabrus enneacanthus Bleeker, 1853. Ambon.

Widespread West Pacific. Sheltered reef crests with dense growth of stinging hydrozoans *Aglaophenia* in which it seeks protection. It rarely leaves its cover, except to move quickly between hydrozoan colonies, but not before having a good look around first to make sure it is safe. It can be distinguished from the other species by the longitudinal lines along its body. It also has 9 spines in the dorsal fin, compared to 10 in similar species. Fin counts are often possible in photographs. Length to 15 cm.

A
P. enneacanthus. Maumere, Flores. Depth 8 m. Length 14 cm.

B
P. enneacanthus. Sangihe Is. D. 5 m. L. 10 cm.

C
P. enneacanthus. Solitary Is., NSW. D. 18 m. L. 10 cm.

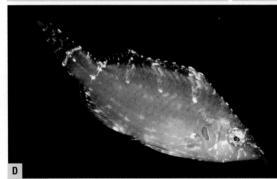
D

E

P. enneacanthus. Sydney Harbour, Australia. Depth 5 m. **D** Length 35 mm. **E** Length 35 mm.

Cheek-bar Wrasse *Pteragogus taeniops*
Cossyphus taeniops Peters, 1855. Mozambique.

A little known species from eastern Africa, known from Inhaca, Mozambique to Zanzibar and recently collected at Aliwal Shoal off South Africa. Reported as living in sheltered weedy habitats. It was photographed on a rocky reef with lots of algae growth in 15 m depth. Variable from dark brown to red, a distinctive bar over the cheek. Ventral fin with a prolonged 1st ray, often reaching well beyond anal-fin origin. Length to 15 cm.

P. taeniops. Kwazulu-Natal, S.A. Depth 15 m. Length 15 cm. Dennis King.

White-barred Sneaky-wrasse
Pteragogus guttatus

Duymaeria guttatus Fowler & Bean, 1928. Philippines.

Widespread Indonesia, Malaysia and Philipines, ranging to Micronesia. Sheltered inner reefs amongst broken coral and rubble. Usually seen in less than 10 m depth, staying well hidden in reefs, but sometimes swimming amongst the long-spined *Diadema* urchins or in thick algae coverage. Best identified by the thin white barring on dorsal fin and upper sides. Length to 9 cm.

A

P. guttatus. Gilimanuk, Bali. Depth 7 m. Length 8 cm.

B

P. guttatus. Pulau Putri, Java. Depth 7 m. Length 9 cm.

C

P. guttatus. Mabul, Malaysia. Depth 4 m. Length 5 cm.

Malachite Wrasse *Pteragogus aurigarius*

Ctenolabrus aurigarius Richardson, 1845. China Seas.
Duymaeria japonica Bleeker, 1856. Nagasaki.

Subtropical Japan and western China seas. Coastal rocky reefs from shallow algal to deep water sponge and soft coral habitats. Adults swim about openly, unlike its congeners. Large males become gaudily coloured with blue and yellow. Length to 22 cm.

A

B

P. aurigarius. Males. Izu, Japan. Depth 7–15 m. Length 22 cm.

C

P. aurigarius. Owase, Japan. Depth 20 m. Length 9 cm.

Masculine. Type species: *Cheilinus trilobatus* Lacepède, 1801. An Indo-Pacific genus comprising about 20 species, several of which appear to be undescribed. A diverse group and in need of revision. Recently the genus *Oxycheilinus* Gill, 1863 (type species: *Cheilinus arenatus* Valenciennes, 1840) was recognised and in general the slender species of *Cheilinus* were assigned to this. Since this does not work for all the species, I have grouped them into two subgenera for the time being, until the taxonomy for the species themselves is sorted out.

Subgenus ***Cheilinus***
  1 *Cheilinus C. abudjubbe* Rüppell, 1835 **Abudjubbe Maori-wrasse** (p. 62)
  2 *?Cheilinus C. bimaculatus* Valenciennes, 1840 **Little Maori-wrasse** (p. 60)
  3 *Cheilinus C. chlorourus* (Bloch, 1791) **White-dotted Maori-wrasse** (p. 62)
  4 *Cheilinus C. fasciatus* (Bloch, 1791) **Banded Maori-wrasse** (p. 64)
  5 *Cheilinus C. lunulatus* (Forsskål, 1775) **Broomtail Maori-wrasse** (p. 63)
  6 *Cheilinus C. oxycephalus* Bleeker, 1853 **Pointhead Maori-wrasse** (p. 61)
  7 *Cheilinus C. quinquecinctus* Rüppell, 1835 **Five-band Maori-wrasse** (p. 64)
  8 *Cheilinus C. trilobatus* Lacepède, 1801 **Triple-tail Maori-wrasse** (p. 63)
  9 *Cheilinus C. undulatus* Rüppell, 1835 **Napoleon Maori-wrasse** (p. 61)
Subgenus ***Oxycheilinus***
  10 *Cheilinus O. arenatus* Valenciennes, 1840 **Thin-line Maori-wrasse** (p. 65)
  11 *Cheilinus O. celebicus* Bleeker, 1853 **Celebes Maori-wrasse** (p. 66)
  12 *Cheilinus O. digramma* (Lacepède, 1801) **Cheek-lined Maori-wrasse** (p. 69)
  13 *Cheilinus O. mentalis* Rüppell, 1835 **Mental Maori-wrasse** (p. 65)
  14 *Cheilinus O. orientalis* Günther, 1862 **Oriental Maori-wrasse** (p. 71)
  15 *Cheilinus O. oxyrhynchus* Bleeker, 1862 **Eared Maori-wrasse** (p. 66)
  16 *Cheilinus O. rhodochrous?* **Thick-line Maori-wrasse** (p. 67)
  17 *Cheilinus O. unifasciatus* Streets, 1877 **Tail-band Maori-wrasse** (p. 68)
  18 *Cheilinus O.* sp 1 **Long-nose Maori-wrasse** (p. 67)
  19 *Cheilinus O.* sp 2 **Caledonian Maori-wrasse** (p. 70)
  20 *Cheilinus O.* sp 3 **Black-tip Maori-wrasse** (p. 70)

Remarks

This genus comprises small to very large species, some are highly secretive and others swim about openly. Most of the small and young of the larger species have colours that function as camouflage, often with complicated patterns of lines or spots. Small species are mostly found amongst seagrass or form schools on algae-rubble flats, whilst the larger species occur on reef crests and slopes. Colour changes with habitat and growth, and some males become gaudily coloured and some fin rays elongate.

All species are easily kept, but the larger species are best kept in either very large aquariums or in public aquariums. Juveniles of the large species grow rapidly and should be avoided for the home aquarium. Their diets comprise a wide range of invertebrates and small fishes. Some of the smaller species are more suited to the home aquarium and are good company for species such as triggers (Balistidae), but bear in mind that they can be aggressive.

Mixed *Cheilinus orientalis* & *C. bimaculatus*. Kalimantan, Indonesia. Roaming open algae-rubble substrates at 20 m depth.

Little Maori-wrasse *Cheilinus bimaculatus*

Cheilinus bimaculatus Valenciennes, 1840. Hawaiian Islands.

Widespread Indo-West Pacific, ranging to sub-tropical regions. Slight geographical variations. Occurs inshore to outer reef lagoons, often in sheltered estuaries and harbours. A common species in algal reef habitats. Small juveniles secretive amongst algae. Variable from brown to yellow or green mixed with various colour shades or spots. Large males usually develop several long filaments on the caudal fin. Length to 15 cm, excluding filaments.

C. bimaculatus. Iriomote, Japan. D. 20 m. L. 85 mm.

C. bimaculatus. **A–C** Males. Bali, Indonesia. D. 3–15 m. L. ~15 cm.

C. bimaculatus. NSW, Australia. **E** Sydney. D. 5 m. L. 14 cm. **F** Montague Island, NSW. D. 25 m. L. 75 mm.

C. bimaculatus. Sydney, Australia. **G** Depth 5 m. Length 12 cm. **H**. Depth. 7 m. Length 55 mm.

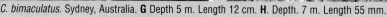

C. bimaculatus. I.O. form. **I** Pulau Weh, Sumatra. D. 15 m. L. 12 cm. Takamasa Tonozuka. **J** Maldives. D. 25 m. L. 10 cm.

Point-head Maori-wrasse
Cheilinus oxycephalus

Cheilinus oxycephalus Bleeker, 1853. Ambon.

Widespread Indo-West Pacific. Coastal and inner reefs, secretive in mixed coral and algae habitats. A shy species, usually found in pairs when adult. Colour highly variable from dark green to brownish red. Head often covered with tiny white spots. Deep-bodied for genus, and snout rather pointed. Length to 17 cm.

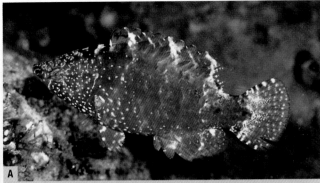

A

C. oxycephalus. Bali. Depth 10 m. Length 15 cm.

B

C. oxycephalus. GBR, Australia. D. 12 m. L. 14 cm.

D

C. oxycephalus. Maldives. Depth 8 m. Length 16 cm.

C

C. oxycephalus. Java. Depth 7 m. Length 12 cm.

Napoleon Wrasse *Cheilinus undulatus*

Cheilinus undulatus Rüppell, 1835. Red Sea.

Widespread Indo-West Pacific. Various reef habitats. Young secretive in algae reef, usually in lagoons amongst dead staghorn corals, or in seagrass. Large adults along outer reef walls or deep coastal slopes. Becomes accustomed to divers or hangs around the back of boats that are returning from fishing and do cleaning in particular places such as outer reef lagoons. Large individuals develop a large hump on the forehead (**A**). Largest member in genus and can reach a length of over 2 m (see page 6).

A

B

C. undulatus. Rowley Shoals, WA.
Depth 5 m. Length 35 mm.

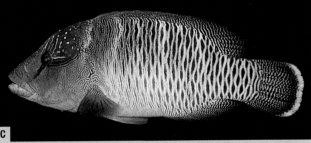

C

C. undulatus. **A** Singapore, Underwater World. **C** Bali. D. 20 m. L. 65 cm.

Abudjubbe Maori-wrasse
Cheilinus abudjubbe

Cheilinus abudjubbe Rüppell, 1835. Red Sea.

Red Sea endemic, closely related to *Cheilinus chlorourus*. Sheltered bays on shallow silty reefs and in mixed coral and algae habitats. Males usually seen swimming along reef margins whilst females and juveniles are more secretive. Identified by the pink to red lines radiating from the eyes and numerous small red spots that gradually change to vertical bars on each scale posteriorly on the body. Length to 40 cm.

C. abudjubbe. **A–C** Egypt, Red Sea. D. 6–12 m. Lengths: **A** male, 38 cm; **B** female, 35 cm; **C** juvenile, 15 cm.

White-dotted Maori-wrasse
Cheilinus chlorourus

Sparus chlorourus Bloch, 1791.
Japan & St Domingo.

Indo-West Pacific. Coastal and inner reefs, often found in shallow harbours and lagoons. Mostly covered with small white spots but these become less distinct in large males which develop long extended lobes on the caudal fin. A series of white blotches along the dorsal fin base and often white on the caudal fin base. Length to 35 cm.

C. chlorourus. Large male. Queensland, Australia. D. 7 m. L. 35 cm.

C. chlorourus. Sulawesi. D. 6 m. L. 15 cm.

C. chlorourus. Male. Maldives. Depth 10 m. Length 35 cm.

C. chlorourus. Monte Bellos, WA. D. 3 m. L. 25 cm.

Triple-tail Maori-wrasse
Cheilinus trilobatus

Cheilinus trilobatus Lacepède, 1801.
Mauritius.

Widespread Indo-West Pacific.
Coastal and inner reefs, often in silty
habitats. Shallow protected areas to
about 10 m depth. Juveniles
secretive on algae reefs and usually
amongst stinging hydrozoans. Adults
recognised by the pattern of fine lines
running vertically over the body
scales. Length to 40 cm.

A

C. trilobatus. Java, Indonesia. Depth 10 m. Length 40 cm.

B

C. trilobatus. Rowley Shoals, WA. D. 8 m. L. 14 cm.

C

C. trilobatus. Tulamben, Bali. Depth 10 m. Length 25 cm.

Broom-tail Maori-wrasse
Cheilinus lunulatus

Labrus lunulatus Forsskål, 1775.
Red Sea.

Endemic to the Red Sea. Closely
related to *Cheilinus trilobatus* from
the Indo-Pacific. Occurs on various
reef habitats to about 25 m depth.
Juveniles secretive in reefs. Adults
identified by their green head,
peculiar 'ear' mark and ragged end of
caudal fin. Length to 45 cm.

A

B

C. lunulatus. Egypt, Red Sea. D. 6–10 m. **A** Male, nuptial colours. Length 45 cm. **B** Young male. Roger Steene.

Sparus fasciatus Bloch, 1791. Japan.

Widespread Indo-West Pacific, but replaced in Red Sea by *Cheilinus quinquecinctus*. Coastal and inner reefs. Young common on silty reefs, usually along edges with algae-rubble and sand. Small juveniles often mistaken for adult *Wetmorella* spp because of their thin vertical white barring. Large individuals develop bright red areas and males have extended caudal fin lobes. Length to 35 cm.

C. fasciatus. Flores, Indonesia. Depth 20 m. Length 32 cm.

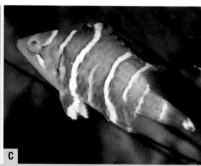

C. fasciatus. Java, Indonesia. **B** Depth 10 m. Length 65 mm. **C** Depth 15 m. Length 40 mm.

Five-band Maori-wrasse
Cheilinus quinquecinctus

Cheilinus quinquecinctus Rüppell, 1835. Red Sea.

Endemic to the Red Sea. Closely related to *Cheilinus fasciatus* from the Indo-Pacific. Occurs on various reef habitats to about 25 m depth. Juveniles secretive on reefs. Adults identified by the red abdominal area, banded pattern and ragged end of caudal fin. Length to 40 cm.

C. quinquecinctus. Egypt, Red Sea. Depth 10 m. Length 35 cm.

C. quinquecinctus. Egypt, Red Sea. **B** Depth 10 m. Length 35 cm. **C** Depth 15 m. Length 40 cm.

Thin-line Maori-wrasse
Cheilinus arenatus

Cheilinus arenatus Valenciennes, 1840. Réunion.

Widespread Indo-West Pacific. Clear outer reef walls with rich invertebrate growth, such as gorgonians or soft corals, at moderate depths over 20 m. Recognised by the thin mid-lateral dark stripe and elongated blotch at front of dorsal fin between 1st and 3rd spines. Length to 15 cm.

C. arenatus. Indonesia. **A** Bali. Depth 45 m. Length 45 mm. **B** Kalimantan. Depth 30 m. Length 15 cm.

Mental-line Maori-wrasse
Cheilinus mentalis

Cheilinus mentalis Rüppell, 1835. Red Sea.

Endemic to the Red Sea. Various coastal to outer reef habitats. Adults mainly along deep water drop-offs, but a common species on inner reefs as well. A slender species, the males have a distinctive black spot on their sides above the pectoral fin base. Length to 20 cm.

C. mentalis. Egypt, Red Sea. **A** & **C** Fully coloured males about 20 cm. **B** Juvenile about 45 mm. **D** & **E** Females about 16–18 cm.

A

C. celebicus. Flores, Indonesia. Depth 15 m. Length 16 cm.

Celebes Maori Wrasse
Cheilinus celebicus

Cheilinus celebicus Bleeker, 1853.
Ujung Padang, southern Sulawesi.

Apparently restricted to Flores and Molucca seas. Records from elsewhere based on *C. oxyrhynchus*. It can be distinguished from the latter by its different colour patterns. The cheek lacks most of the multiple lines below the eye and the dorsal fin has two thin, usually irregular, red marginal lines (**C**). Found on inner reef slopes with a rich mix of soft and brittle hard corals and other invertebrates. Usually in depths from 10 to 40 m, but occasionally in shallower water. Length to 18 cm.

B

C

C. celebicus. Flores, Indonesia. **B** Fully coloured male. Depth 15 m. Length 18 cm. **C** Depth 25 m. Length 6 cm.

A

C. oxyrhynchus. Fully coloured male. Bali, Indonesia. Depth 10 m. Length 20 cm.

Eared Maori Wrasse
Cheilinus oxyrhynchus

Cheilinus oxyrhynchus Bleeker, 1862.
Sulawesi, Ambon & Batjan (Bacan).
Cheilinus hoeveni Bleeker, 1862. Ambon.

West Pacific, Japan to Andaman Sea along Wallace's Line, northern Moluccen Sea, and to north-eastern Australia. Sheltered coastal and inner reefs in rich coral habitats. Similar to *Cheilinus celebicus*, but has multiple lines below the eye, a powdery pattern on the upper sides of the body, and males with white 'ear' spot (also faint in females) and single red marginal line in dorsal fin. Length to 20 cm.

B

C

C. oxyrhynchus. Java, Indonesia. **B** Depth 7 m. Length 15 cm. **C** Depth 7 m. Length 10 cm.

Long-nose Maori-wrasse *Cheilinus* sp 1

An apparently undescribed species that is widespread in Indonesia and New Guinea. Occurs on clear coastal to outer reef rubble slopes with rich growth of algae and brittle hard corals. Has a long nose and small ocelli or black spot on tail-base. Length to 16 cm.

A

C. sp 1. Java, Indonesia. L. 35 mm.

B

C. sp 1 Flores, Indonesia. Depth 20 m. Length 8 cm.

C

C. sp 1. Milne Bay, PNG. D. 18 m. L. 16 cm.

D

C. sp 1. Flores, Indonesia. Depth 20 m. Length 14 cm.

Thick-stripe Maori-wrasse
Cheilinus rhodochrous

Cheilinus rhodochrous
Playfair & Günther, 1867. Zanzibar.

Tentative identification. Widespread Indo-West Pacific. Coastal to outer reef habitats. Juveniles often in crinoids or soft corals at moderate depths. Adults swim along reef slopes. Small juveniles with a series of ocelli on tail along mid-lateral line. Length to 20 cm.

A

C. rhodochrous. Flores, Indonesia. Depth 10 m. Length 15 cm.

B

C. rhodochrous. Bali. D. 25 m. L. 25 mm.

C

C. rhodochrous. Sydney. D. 4 m. L. 45 mm.

D

C. rhodochrous. Maldives. Depth 20 m. Length 20 cm.

Cheilinus unifasciatus Streets, 1877
Line Islands, central Pacific.

Widespread Indo-West Pacific. Clear coastal to outer reef habitats. Young secretive in soft corals or hydrozoans. Adults swim close to reefs, although large males move over large areas, often well above the substrate, and display a bright white band over the tail. Length to 30 cm.

A

C. unifasciatus. Iriomote, Japan. Depth 20 m. Length 30 cm.

B

C. unifasciatus. Iriomote, Japan. Depth 20 m. Length 24 cm.

C

C. unifasciatus. Juvenile. Kochi, Japan. Depth 10 m.
Length 6 cm. Tomonori Hirata.

D

C. unifasciatus. Rowley Shoals, WA. D. 10 m. L. 20 cm.

E

C. unifasciatus. Juvenile. Kochi, Japan. Depth 8 m.
Length 6 cm. Tomonori Hirata.

F

G

C. unifasciatus. GBR. Australia. **F** Female. Length 16 cm. **G** Juvenile. Length 9 cm. Phil Woodhead.

Cheek-lined Maori-wrasse
Cheilinus digramma

Labrus digrammus Lacepède, 1801.
Mauritius.

Widespread Indo-West Pacific. Adults occur in various coastal to outer reef habitats. Young are closer to the shore on sheltered reef crests or slopes, usually amongst soft corals or stinging hydrozoans. Juveniles plain grey to reddish brown with yellowish tail. Adults ornamented with various bright colours. Tail yellow in females and changing to blue in males. Length to about 35 cm.

A

C. digramma. Male. GBR, Australia. Depth 10 m. Length 34 cm.

B

C. digramma. Java, Indonesia. Depth 6 m. Length 10 cm.

C

C. digramma. Male. Kerama, Japan. Depth 20 m. Length 30 cm.

D

C. digramma. Flores, Indonesia. Depth 10 m. Length 12 cm.

E

C. digramma. Male. Kerama, Japan. Depth 20 m. Length 30 cm.

F

C. digramma. PNG. Depth 20 m. Length 20 cm.

G

C. digramma. Female. Milne Bay, PNG. Depth 10 m. Length 25 cm.

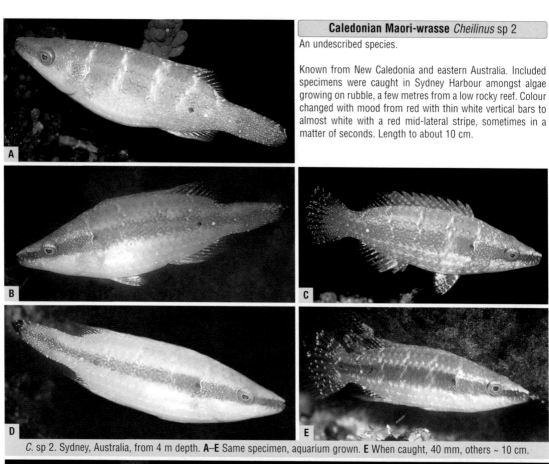

Caledonian Maori-wrasse *Cheilinus* sp 2

An undescribed species.

Known from New Caledonia and eastern Australia. Included specimens were caught in Sydney Harbour amongst algae growing on rubble, a few metres from a low rocky reef. Colour changed with mood from red with thin white vertical bars to almost white with a red mid-lateral stripe, sometimes in a matter of seconds. Length to about 10 cm.

C. sp 2. Sydney, Australia, from 4 m depth. **A–E** Same specimen, aquarium grown. **E** When caught, 40 mm, others ~ 10 cm.

C. sp 2. Sydney, Australia. Same individual as above, demonstrating its amazing ability to change colour.

Black-tip Maori-wrasse *Cheilinus* sp 3

An undescribed species.

Known from Indonesia but is probably more widespread. Occurs along deep slopes and sand flats adjacent to reefs. Usually seen in small groups amongst sparse reef and algae patches. In natural light, the submarginal red and black lines on the caudal fin form a distinct black spot when the fin is held closed. Length to about 10 cm.

A

B

C

C. sp 3. Indonesia. Depth 12–15 m. **A** Lembeh Strait. Length 10 cm. **B** Java. Length 85 mm. **C** Java. Length 40 mm.

Slender Maori-wrasse *Cheilinus orientalis*

Cheilinus orientalis Günther, 1862.
Based on Bleeker's *C. coccineus*, from Bacan (Batjan).

Northern Indonesia to southern Japan. Male usually has black blotch between dorsal origin and lateral line. Females swim in small groups on deep open sandy substrates with sparse reef comprising rubble and algae. Often with other small wrasses that also favour this habitat. Length to about 12 cm.

A

C. orientalis. Kochi, Japan. D. 25 m. L. 3 cm. T. Hirata.

B

C. orientalis. Kalimantan, Indonesia. D. 20 m. L. 8 cm.

C

C. orientalis. Kochi, Japan. D. 40 m. L. 4 cm. T. Hirata.

D

C. orientalis. Okinawa, Japan. D. 35 m. L. to 10 cm. Shinya Inoue.

SUBFAMILY CHEILIONAE - GENUS *Cheilio* Lacepède, 1802

Masculine. Type species: *Cheilio auratus* Lacepède, 1802. (= *Labrus inermis* Forsskål, 1775). A single species, but Red Sea population is uniquely coloured, and the true species. Other populations may be subspecific.

A

B

Labrus inermis Forsskål, 1775. Red Sea.

Widespread Indo-West Pacific, ranging to subtropical waters. Occurs in estuaries, coastal bays and lagoons with seagrasses, as well as on reef crests with rich soft coral growth. Juveniles secretive in seagrasses or attached to *Sargassum*. Adults usually in small loose aggregations, but occasionally they form large schools to spawn. Variable, green to yellow or brown. Red Sea males have black tails. Length to 50 cm.

C

D

C. inermis. Egypt, Red Sea. Depth 20 m. **A** & **B** Females, 35–40 cm long. **C** & **D** Males, 40 cm long.

E

C. inermis. Male swimming with goatfish, *Parupeneus heptacanthus*. Milne Bay, PNG. Depth 8 m. Length 40 cm.

F

G

C. inermis. Flores, Indonesia. Depth 6 m. Length 20 cm.

C. inermis. Sydney Harbour, Australia. D. 3 m. L. 15 cm.

Pseudolabrus 74

Notolabrus 81

Pictilabrus 88

Eupetrichthys 91

Austrolabrus 92

Dotalabrus 93

SUBFAMILY JULININAE - Pseudolabrines-related, Genera Contents

Suezichthys (Nelabrichthys) 95

Suezichthys (Suezichthys) 99

Masculine. Type species: *Labrus rubiginosus* Temminck & Schlegel, 1845. This species is now known as *Pseudolabrus sieboldi* and only recently redescribed when the species from East Asian waters were revised by Kohji Mabuchi & Tetsuji Nakabo in 1997. A small Indo-Pacific genus with 11 species, of which two occur in the northern hemisphere and nine in the southern hemisphere.

1 *Pseudolabrus biserialis* (Klunzinger, 1879) **Red-band Wrasse** (p. 79)
2 *Pseudolabrus eoethinus* (Richardson, 1846) **Canton Wrasse** (p. 77)
3 *Pseudolabrus fuentesi* (Regan, 1913) **Fuentes's Wrasse** (N.A.)
4 *Pseudolabrus gayi* (Valenciennes, 1839) **Gay's Wrasse** (N.A.)
5 *Pseudolabrus guentheri* Bleeker, 1862 **Günther's Wrasse** (p. 75)
6 *Pseudolabrus luculentus* (Richardson, 1848) **Luculentus Wrasse** (p. 78)
7 *Pseudolabrus miles* (Bloch & Schneider, 1801) **New Zealand Scarlet Wrasse** (p. 79)
8 *Pseudolabrus psittaculus* (Richardson, 1840) **Rosy Wrasse** (p. 80)
9 *Pseudolabrus semifasciatus* (Rendahl, 1921) **Half-barred Wrasse** (this page)
10 *Pseudolabrus sieboldi* Mabuchi & Nakabo, 1997 **Siebold's Wrasse** (p. 76)
11 *Pseudolabrus torotai* Russell & Randall, 1981 **Rapa Wrasse** (N.A.)

Pseudolabrus semifasciatus. Aquarium. From Easter Island. Length c. 23 cm. Kiyoshi Endoh.

A little known species from Easter Island. It occurs around rocky reefs and one specimen was reported as being caught from 250 m depth. Length to 25 cm. A similar species, *P. torotai*, has black bars instead of saddles and is known from Rapa Island, but few specimens of both species are known and *P. torotai* may possibly represent just a variation or the female form.

The various species are distributed over subtropical to temperate zones from about 20° north and south of the equator to about 35° north and at most 40° south, but one species to almost 50° south in New Zealand. The more tropical species can reach a length of about 20 cm, whilst the ones living in cooler climates can reach 30 cm. They feature large cycloid scales on the body which extend into a narrow sheath along dorsal and anal fin bases. Most species can be found on shallow algae-rock reefs, but some range to depths of over 100 m. Small juveniles live secretively amongst algae and are well camouflaged. Adults swim about openly and occur in small loose groups, usually comprising subadults and females that are distributed over reef-sections, and dominated by a large male. Males derive from the group, usually the largest female that undergoes a sex-change after the dominating male disappears. All the species are easily kept in captivity but require plenty of space with lots of rocks. Diet can be a mixture of meaty foods but large individuals will take to small fishes if kept with them. Many favour small molluscs or worms. They are territorial and it is best to introduce several individuals at the same time, rather that adding one later as it may be rejected, and preferably start with juveniles.

Günther's Wrasse *Pseudolabrus guentheri*

Pseudolabrus Güntheri Bleeker, 1862. Australia.

Only found on the eastern Australian coast from southern Queensland to southern New South Wales. A common species in the Sydney region in bays and coastal waters on rocky reefs with good algae growth. Variable from orange-brown to green and a lined or barred pattern that is similar for both sexes. Length to 18 cm.

A

P. guentheri. Sydney Harbour, Australia. Depth 5 m. Length 18 cm.

B

C

P. guentheri. **B** Sydney, Australia. Depth 7 m. Length 6 cm. **C** Montague Island, Australia. Depth 25 m. Length 18 cm.

D

E

P. guentheri. Sydney, Australia. **D** Depth 15 m. Length 12 cm. **E** Depth 5 m. Length 16 cm.

F

P. guentheri. Sydney, Australia. Depth 3 m. Length 16 cm.

Pseudolabrus sieboldi. Male, length about 15 cm. Owase, Japan.

Pseudolabrus sieboldi Mabuchi & Nakabo, 1997. Ehime Prefecture, Japan.

Occurs on the coast of southern Japan and Taiwan. According to the above authors it is most common on the Sea of Japan coast and inhabits rocky reefs in less than 100 m depth. At Osezaki this species was observed in small loose groups of subadults and single juveniles. Length to 20 cm.

P. sieboldi. Kochi. D. 20 m. L. 2 cm. T. Hirata.

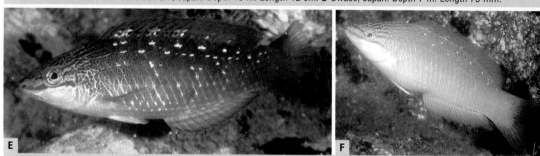

P. sieboldi. **B** Izu Oceanic Park, Japan. Depth 15 m. Length 12 cm. **D** Owase, Japan. Depth 7 m. Length 75 mm.

P. sieboldi. **E** Female. Kochi, Japan. Depth 5 m. Length 10 cm. Tomonori Hirata. **F** Osezaki, Japan. Depth 6 m. Length 11 cm.

P. sieboldi. Osezaki, Japan. Depth 12 m. Length 18 cm.

Canton Wrasse *Pseudolabrus eoethinus*

Labrus eöthinus Richardson, 1846. Canton, China.

Pacific coast of southern Japan to the Ogasawara Islands and coast of China. Occurs on shallow rocky and coral reefs to about 30 m depth. Variable in colour from brown-red to yellow. Lacks the white spots of *Pseudolabrus sieboldi* and both species were referred to as *P. japonicus* until corrected by Mabuchi & Nakabo, 1997. Length to 23 cm.

A

B
P. eoethinus. Ehime. D. 8 m. L. 15 mm. T. Hirata.

C
P. eoethinus. Kochi. D. 8 m. L. 10 cm. T. Hirata.

E

P. eoethinus. Female. Kochi, Japan. Depth 2 m. Length 16 cm. Tomonori Hirata.

D

P. eoethinus. Male. Ehime, Japan. Depth 3 m. Length 18 cm. Tomonori Hirata.

F

P. eoethinus. **E** Female. Owase, Japan. Depth 15 m. Length 16 cm. **F** Kochi, Japan. Depth 8 m. Length 20 cm. Tomonori Hirata.

G
P. eoethinus. Nuptial colours, male. Izu Oceanic Park, Japan. Depth 12 m. Length 22 cm.

Labrus luculentus Richardson, 1848. Australia.

Eastern Australia to Norfolk Island and islands of north-eastern New Zealand. Clear coastal waters on rocky reefs to at least 50 m depth. Usually seen singly, but often various individuals are spread over large reef areas. Females brown to orange with thin white diagonal lines over abdomen. Males with alternating white and black blotches along dorsal fin base. Length to 20 cm.

A

P. luculentus. Female. Montague I., Australia. Depth 25 m. Length 16 cm.

C

P. luculentus. Sydney, Australia. D. 5 m. L. 55 mm.

B

D

P. luculentus. **B** Bermagui, Australia. Depth 20 m. Length 18 cm. **D** Sydney, Australia. Depth 7 m. Length 85 mm.

E

F

P. luculentus. **E** Male. Sydney, Australia. Depth 5 m. Length 16 cm. **F** Male. Bermagui, Australia. Depth 17 m. Length 20 cm.

G

P. luculentus. Male. Bermagui, Australia. Depth 20 m. Length 19 cm.

Red-band Wrasse *Pseudolabrus biserialis*

Labrichthys biserialis Klunzinger, 1879.
King Georges Sound, Western Australia.

Only known from south-western Australia. Occurs on clear coastal rocky reef with good algae coverage to about 20 m depth. Readily identified by colour. Males have a bright red anal fin. Length to 21 cm.

P. biserialis. **A** King Georges Sound, W. A. Depth 2 m. Length 10 cm. **B** Male. Esperance. W.A. Depth 5 m. Length 20 cm.

P. biserialis. **C** Canal Rocks, W. A. Depth 7 m. Length 10 cm. **D** Female. Busselton. W.A. Depth 4 m. Length 16 cm.

Scarlet Wrasse *Pseudolabrus miles*

Labrus miles Bloch & Schneider, 1801. New Zealand.

Only known from the New Zealand region where it is widespread and ranges far south. The most temperate species in the genus. Occurs on rocky-boulder reefs to about 40 m depth. Easily identified by the black mark over the base of the caudal fin. Largest species in the genus, length to 40 cm.

P. miles. Napier Aquarium, New Zealand, Length 35 cm.

P. miles. Male. Napier Aquarium, New Zealand, Length 35 cm.

79

Labrus psittaculus Richardson, 1840. Tasmania.
Labrichthys Mortoni Johnston, 1885. Tasmania.

Only known from south-eastern Australia, ranging west to South Australia, and Tasmania. Adults mainly on open coastal reefs at moderate depths over 20 m, but juveniles may inhabit bays on the ocean side in shallow water. Juveniles have a black peduncular spot with white at both ends. Males are plain with yellow longitudinal lines along lower side, following scale rows. Length to 23 cm.

P. psittaculus. Male. Bicheno, Tasmania. Depth 35 m. Length 23 cm.

P. psittaculus. Melbourne, Australia. **B** Depth 10 m. Length 16 cm. **C** Depth 7 m. Length 75 mm.

P. psittaculus. **B** Melbourne, Australia. Depth 10 m. Length 14 cm. **C** Bermagui, NSW. Depth 25 m. Length 15 cm.

P. psittaculus. Male. Derwent River, Tasmania. Depth 15 m. Length 23 cm.

Masculine. Type species: *Labrus fucicola* Richardson, 1840. A small Australian - New Zealand genus with 7 species, which were prior to Russell, 1988, included in the genus *Pseudolabrus*.

1 *Notolabrus celidotus* (Bloch & Schneider, 1801) **Spotty** (p. 87)
2 *Notolabrus cinctus* (Hutton, 1877) **Girdled Wrasse** (p. 87)
3 *Notolabrus fucicola* (Richardson, 1840) **Purple Wrasse** (p. 82)
4 *Notolabrus gymnogenis* (Günther, 1862) **Crimson-banded Wrasse** (p. 85)
5 *Notolabrus inscriptus* (Richardson, 1848) **Inscribed Wrasse** (p. 86)
6 *Notolabrus parilus* (Richardson, 1850) **Orange-spotted Wrasse** (p. 84)
7 *Notolabrus tetricus* (Richardson, 1840) **Blue-throat Wrasse** (p. 83)

Pseudolabrus gymnogenus. The more tropical and colourful member of the genus. Male, length about 40 cm. Sydney, Australia.

The various species are distributed over subtropical to temperate zones of Australia and New Zealand, with one ranging into Queensland. One species is found in Western Australia, three are endemic to Australia and two are endemic to New Zealand, whilst two species occur in both regions. *Notolabrus* is distinguishable from *Pseudolabrus* by a number of characteristics that are not readily obvious and some are related to the skeleton or teeth. Most species grow quite large, reaching 60 cm. Males are usually coloured differently from females and some are very colourful. Although these fishes are easily kept in captivity, they grow large and require very large homes. Adults are best assigned to public aquariums. Many hobbyists catch juveniles, keep them until they outgrow their home and then release them back into the wild. They feed on a variety of invertebrates, some favouring molluscs and other crustaceans that are living amongst rubble or algae. Some will follow large rays that disturb the sea bed to grab crabs trying to escape or worms that may be exposed.

Most species are common in coastal rocky habitats and are often dominant reef species. Some favour high energy zones with kelp forests and swim just under the foaming surface waters where the swell smashes into the shore. Adults travel large areas of reef and may go down to great depths. Some are commonly found to 40 m but are sometimes trawled in depths over 150 m. Juveniles are found in quieter bays in shallow water amongst algae or in seagrass and reef mixed habitats, sometimes in small aggregations. Sometimes hybrids occur when two species are spawning simultaneously in the same area and their pelagic gametes mix.

Yellow-saddled Wrasse *Notolabrus fucicola*

Labrus fucicola Richardson, 1840. Tasmania.

Widespread in south-eastern Australia and New Zealand. Mainly found on kelp reefs, often in shallow, turbulent coastal zones but also in deeper waters on offshore reefs to 90 m. Small juveniles in large coastal rockpools or open estuaries. Males with cream to yellow blotches over the back. Females and juveniles usually green to brown with dusky banding. Length to 45 cm. Known in NZ as Banded Wrasse.

N. fucicola. Flinders, Vic. Rockpool. Length 15 mm.

N. fucicola. Male. Montague I, NSW. Depth 2 m. Length 40 cm.

N. fucicola. **B** Montague I, NSW. Depth 2 m. Length 40 cm. **D** Kent-group Bass Strait. Depth 25 m. Length 15 cm.

N. fucicola. Females. Montague I, NSW. Depth 2 m. Length 30–35 cm.

Hybrids. *N. fucicola* X *tetricus.* **F** Bicheno, Tasmania. Depth 30 m. Length 45 cm. **G** Bermagui, NSW. Depth 25 m. Length 50 cm.

Blue-throat Wrasse *Notolabrus tetricus*

Labrus tetricus Richardson, 1840. Tasmania.

Widespread south-eastern Australia from southern Tasmania to NSW and SA. Adults mainly on open coast reefs and rocky shores at moderate depths to 40 m and reported to 160 m. Juveniles commonly found on algae reefs on the ocean side of estuaries. Males distinctly coloured and usually recognised by their broad white band. Juveniles bright green to brown or grey with some banding. Subadults have a dark band centrally on the body. Length to 60 cm.

N. tetricus. Male. Melbourne, Victoria. Depth 10 m. Length 50 cm.

N. tetricus. **B** Juvenile. Melbourne, Victoria. Depth 4 m. Length 65 mm. **C** Female. Kangaroo I., SA. Depth 5 m. Length 45 cm.

N. tetricus. Melbourne, Victoria. **B** Juvenile. Depth 3 m. Length 45 mm. **C** Females. Depth 5 m. Length 30 cm.

N. tetricus. Male. Kangaroo I., SA. Depth 5 m. Length 55 cm.

Orange-spotted Wrasse *Notolabrus parilus*

Tautoga parila Richardson, 1850. Western Australia.

Widespread in south-western Australia, ranging north to Shark Bay and east to Kangaroo Island in SA. Stragglers may reach Victoria. Occurs in shallow weed and sponge habitats in coastal bays or islands. Juveniles brown or green with indistinct dusky bands, developing patches of orange spots in the pale areas on their back. Large adults with small orange spots and males with a pale mid-lateral streak. Length to 35 cm.

N. parilus. Male. Recherche Archipelago, WA. Depth 4 m. Length 35 cm.

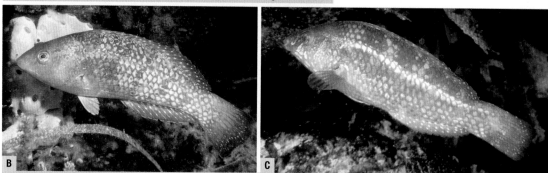

N. parilus. **B** Kangaroo I., SA. Depth 20 m. Length 20 cm. **C** Carnac I., WA. Depth 5 m. Length 25 cm.

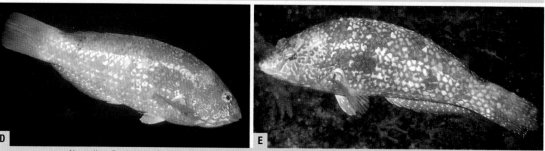

N. parilus. Recherche Archipelago, WA. **D** Depth 15 m. Length 30 cm. **E** Depth 5 m. Length 25 cm.

N. parilus. Male. Recherche Archipelago, WA. Depth 4 m. Length 35 cm.

Crimson-banded Wrasse *Notolabrus gymnogenis*

Labrichthys gymnogenis Günther, 1862. Sydney.

Widespread New South Wales coast, ranging into southern Queensland and northern Victoria. A few reported from Lord Howe Island. Occurs on rocky reefs with sparse algae growth and ranges to a moderate depth where sponges are prominent. Juveniles and females greenish grey to brown. Females in deep water more red. Males have yellow pectorals and bright red soft dorsal and anal fins. Length to 40 cm.

A

N. gymnogenis. Male. Bermagui, NSW. Depth 20 m. Length 40 cm.

B

C

N. gymnogenis. Sydney, NSW. **B** Juvenile. Depth 4 m. Length 14 cm. **C** Changing sex. Depth 12 m. Length 35 cm.

D

E

N. gymnogenis. Montague I., NSW. **D** Female. Depth 25 m. Length 24 cm. **E** Female. Depth 12 m. Length 35 cm.

F

N. gymnogenis. Male. Montague Island, NSW. Depth 24 m. Length 40 cm.

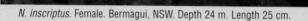

Labrus inscriptus, vel *Tautoga inscriptus*
Richardson, 1848. Norfolk Island.

Widespread from north-eastern New Zealand and
Kermadec Islands to Norfolk and Lord Howe Island
and NSW, but rare in latter. Occurs primarily on
kelp-rock reefs, ranging to sponge reefs to about
25 m depth. Juveniles green to brown with pale
thin lines along scale rows. Males dark green to
grey-blue with small yellow dots. Length to 36 cm.

Called Green Wrasse in NZ.

N. inscriptus. Female. Bermagui, NSW. Depth 24 m. Length 25 cm.

N. inscriptus. **B** Napier Aquarium, NZ. Length 30 cm. **C** & **D** Baraga Bay, NSW. Depth 5 m. Length 12 cm.

N. inscriptus. Large male. Ned's Beach, Lord Howe Island. Depth 10 m. Malcolm Francis.

Spotty *Notolabrus celidotus*

Labrus celidotus Bloch & Schneider, 1801.
New Zealand.

Occurs throughout New Zealand coastal waters and is often abundant on inshore rocky reefs. Mainly found in less exposed areas and estuaries where females may form aggregations. Usually in shallow waters, to 10 m depth, but reported as deep as 145 m. Juveniles vary from green to brown, matching seaweed colour of the area, with an obvious large dark spot on the body that also features in females. Males with higher placed, smaller spots. Length to 30 cm.

A

N. celidotus. Unusually coloured male. Napier Aquarium, New Zealand. L. 27 cm.

B

C

N. celidotus. Napier Aquarium, New Zealand. **B** Female colour. Length 16 cm. **C** Male. Length 24 cm.

Girdled Wrasse *Notolabrus cinctus*

Labrichthys cincta Hutton, 1877. New Zealand.

Only known from the New Zealand region where widespread but more common in the southern areas and ranges south to sub-antarctic islands. Usually occurs in moderate depths to about 40 m and recorded to almost 100 m depth. Colour of adults is plain grey, pale-centred scales and a distinctive dark band centrally on the body. No difference reported between the sexes. Juveniles similar but match weed colours and lack the dark band on the body. Length to 41 cm.

A

N. cinctus. Secretary I., New Zealand. Malcolm Francis.

B

N. cinctus. George Sd., New Zealand. Malcolm Francis.

C

N. cinctus. Pukeokaoka I., New Zealand. Malcolm Francis.

Masculine. Type species: *Labrus laticlavius* Richardson, 1839. A small Australian genus with 3 species, one of which was tentatively included by Hutchins & Morrison, 1996.

1 *Pictilabrus brauni* Hutchins & Morrison, 1996 **Braun's Wrasse** (p. 90)
2 *Pictilabrus laticlavius* (Richardson, 1839) **Senator Wrasse** (p. 89)
3 *Pictilabrus viridis* Russell, 1988 **Green Senator Wrasse** (p. 90)

One species is widespread along Australia's southern coast from about 30°S, and two more species have a restricted distribution in south-western Australia. *Pictilabrus* is distinct from the closely related *Pseudolabrus* by its smaller head and other, but less obvious characteristics. Males are usually coloured differently from females and some are very colourful. Colours vary somewhat with habitat and those in a red-algae dominated environment are brown or red and those in a green-algae dominated one are yellow to green. The species are locally common in coastal rocky habitats, some favouring sheltered bays and harbours, but they also occur in high energy zones that are battered by large oceanic southern swells. Juveniles are somewhat secretive on algae reefs. Adults occur in shallow weed habitats as well as deep on sponge or invertebrate-rich reefs.

Of the three species, only *Pictilabrus laticlavius* is regularly collected and they are easily kept wrasses that feed on all meaty-type foods offered. They are best suited to the community and larger aquariums. In the wild they feed on a variety of invertebrates that crawl amongst rubble or algae, including crustaceans and worms. The other two smaller species are more habitat specific and may need special care, but there is no aquarium information available. Both species live in clear, oceanic water and often in swell-exposed high-energy zones with heavily vegetated rocks.

Pictilabrus laticlavius. The type-species for the genus. Male, length about 26 cm. Bermagui, NSW.

Senator Wrasse *Pictilabrus laticlavius*

Labrus laticlavius Richardson, 1839. Tasmania.

Widespread along Australia's southern coast and estuaries from northern NSW to southern Tasmania and on the west coast north to Kalbarri. Occurs primarily on algae and weed covered rocky reefs but also inhabits deeper water where sponges and weeds are mixed to about 30 m depth. Abundant in some areas. General colouration is green to reddish brown, resembling the local weed colours. Juveniles greenish with pearly blue spots and females brown to reddish brown. Males distinguished by their gaudy colours. Length to 30 cm.

A

P. laticlavius. Male. Sydney, NSW. Depth 7 m. Length 25 cm.

B

C

P. laticlavius. **B** Bermagui, NSW. Depth 22 m. Length 15 cm. **C** Kangaroo I., SA. Depth 7 m. Length 27 cm.

D

E

P. laticlavius. **D** Bermagui, NSW. Depth 22 m. Length 15 cm. **E** Melbourne, Vic. Depth 7 m. Length 23 cm.

F

P. laticlavius. Male. Nine-pin Point, Tasmania. Depth 15 m. Length 30 cm.

Green Senator Wrasse *Pictilabrus viridis*

Pictilabrus viridis Russell, 1988. Western Australia.

Distribution is very restricted to the south-west corner of Western Australia. It occurs around rocky outcrops exposed to ocean swells, usually at a few metres depth. It was discovered by the author on his honeymoon in 1978 who borrowed Russell's small spear to collect the first specimens, and the description followed 10 years later. Most individuals appear bright green in natural light. Length to 15 cm.

P. viridis. Lucky Bay, WA (type-locality). Depth 2 m. Length 15 cm.

P. viridis. Lucky Bay, WA. **B** Male. Depth 5 m. Length 15 cm. **C** Female. Depth 7 m. Length 14 cm.

P. viridis. **D** Female. Lucky Bay, WA. Depth 5 m. Length 12 cm. **E** Male. Recherche Archipelago. Depth 12 m. Length 15 cm.

Braun's Senator Wrasse *Pictilabrus brauni*

Pictilabrus brauni Hutchins & Morrison, 1996. W. A.

Only known from a small region on the south coast of Western Australia, but it is secretive and it resembles juveniles of the more common wrasses. It may have gone unnoticed in adjacent areas. Occurs in heavily vegetated rocky reefs in the shallows, where the females occur in small loose aggregations. A small species, the largest specimen is only 10 cm long.

P. brauni. South Western Australia. **A** & **B** Males, in aquarium. L. 10 cm. **C** Females. D. 7 m. L. 85 mm. **A–C** Barry Hutchins.

90

GENUS *Eupetrichthys* Ramsay & Ogilby, 1888

Masculine. Type species: *Eupetrichthys angustipes* Richardson, 1839. A monotypic Australian genus.

Snake-skin Wrasse *Eupetrichthys angustipes*

Eupetrichthys angustipes Richardson, 1839. Sydney.

Widespread along Australia's mainland southern coast from NSW to WA, but rare in the Bass Strait region. Easily identified by its colour and elongated body. Often moves along with tail dragging on the sea bed. Occurs on rubble and rock reefs with sparse algae in coastal waters and in harbours to 40 m depth. Length to 15 cm.

E. angustipes. Male. Sydney, NSW. D. 10 m. L. 14 cm.

E. angustipes. Kangaroo I., SA. D. 20 m. L. 10 cm.

E. angustipes. Jervis Bay, NSW. D. 12 m. L. 12 cm.

E. angustipes. Courting. NSW. Male, darkest ~15 cm.

E. angustipes. Lucky Bay, Western Australia. D. 7 m. L. 12 cm.

E. angustipes. **F** Male. Seal Rocks, NSW. Depth 5 m. Length 15 cm. **G** Sydney Harbour, NSW. Depth 4 m. Length 12 cm.

Masculine. Type species: *Labrichthys maculata* Macleay, 1881. A monotypic Australian genus.

A

A. maculatus. Male. Esperance, WA. D. 7 m. L. 16 cm.

Black-spotted Wrasse *Austrolabrus maculatus*

Labrichthys maculata Macleay, 1881.
King Georges Sound, Western Australia.

Known from Shark Bay, WA, to Kangaroo I., SA, and a separate population in NSW along most of its coast. Western form occurs on shallow rocky reefs and rubble substrates to about 20 m depth, whilst the eastern ones are usually found much deeper, to 40 m, in sponge habitats. Juveniles in shallower waters in algae rock-boulder habitats. Pinkish brown with black spots scattered over the back. A white-edged black peduncular saddle that fades in large adults. Length to 20 cm.

B

C

A. maculatus. **B** Male, Rapid bay, SA. D. 9 m. L. 17 cm. **C** Kangaroo I., SA. D. 12 m. L. 10 cm.

D

E

A. maculatus. Male. nuptial colours. Sydney, NSW. D. 7 m. L. 14 cm.   *A. maculatus*. Seal Rocks, NSW. D. 5 m. L. 6 cm.

F

G

A. maculatus. Male. Sydney, NSW. D. 7 m. L. 18 cm.   *A. maculatus*. Seal Rocks, NSW. D. 10 m. L. 7 cm.

GENUS *Dotalabrus* Whitley, 1930

Masculine. Type species: *Cheilinus aurantiacus* Castelnau, 1872. A small Australian genus with two species. One widespread along the south coast and the other with a restricted distribution in the south west corner of Western Australia. Both occur on rocky reefs with dense vegetation or in seagrasses. Small species that adapts very well to the home aquarium and becomes extremely tame.

Pretty Polly *Dotalabrus aurantiacus*

Cheilinus aurantiacus Castelnau, 1872.
St. Vincent Gulf, SA.

Southern coast from Bass Strait to Western Australia. Occurs in large seagrass beds and heavily vegetated reefs in sheltered bays and open estuaries. Often swims almost vertically just above the seagrasses. Grey to bright green or near black with blotched or barred patterns. Length to 14 cm.

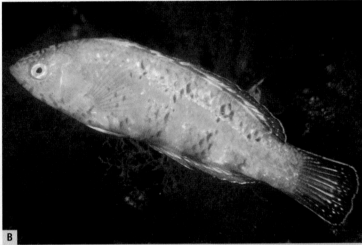

D. aurantiacus. Port Philip Bay, Victoria. **A** Juvenile. Length 45 mm. **B** Nuptial male. Depth 4 m. Length 14 cm.

D. aurantiacus. Kangaroo I., SA. **C** Depth 4 m. Length 10 cm. **D** Depth 18 m. Length 12 cm

D. aurantiacus. Variations. **E** Lucky Bay, WA. Depth 12 m. Length 12 cm. **F** & **G** Portsea, Vic. Depth 4 m. Length 14 cm

Dotalabrus alleni Russell, 1988. Carnac I., WA.

Only known from the south-west corner of Western Australia. Occurs on kelp reefs, usually forming small aggregations comprising females and a dominating male. Females swim close to the substrate but males less so and are more obvious by their bright colours. Juveniles green with a pattern of dark bars over the back that extend as spots below. A small species, reaching just 11 cm in length.

D. alleni. Male. Lucky Bay, WA. D. 7 m. L. 10 cm.

D. alleni. Female. Lucky Bay, WA. D. 7 m. L. 9 cm.

D. alleni. Male. Lucky Bay, WA. D. 12 m. L. 11 cm.

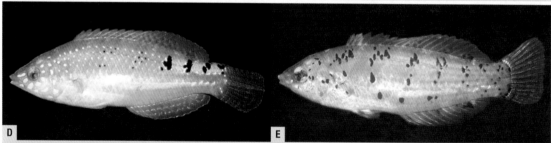

D. alleni. Lucky Bay, WA. **D** Male. Depth 12 m. Length 10 cm. **E** Female. Depth 12 m. Length 8 cm.

D. alleni. Male and several females, as typically seen in Lucky Bay, WA. Depth 10 m.

Masculine. Type species: *Labrichthys caudovittatus* Steindachner, 1898. A small Indo-Pacific genus with 11 species, but the taxonomy of this genus is confused due to few specimens being available and uniformity in morphology between some of the species. Russell revised the genus for the Indo-Pacific in 1985, adding a species in 1986, but *Labrus ornatus* from the Atlantic was not included. Dividable into two groups with 1.5 or 2.5 scale rows above the lateral line.

2.5 scales above lateral line (*Nelabrichthys*)
1 *Suezichthys arquatus* Russell, 1985 **Painted Rainbow-wrasse** (p. 96)
2 *Suezichthys bifurcatus* Russell, 1986 **Striped Trawl-wrasse** (p. 98)
3 *Suezichthys cyanolaemus* Russell, 1985 **Blue-throated Rainbow-wrasse** (p. 98)
4 *Suezichthys notatus* (Kamohara, 1958) **Northern Painted Rainbow-wrasse** (p. 97)
5 *Suezichthys ornatus* (Carmichae, 1818) **Tristan Rainbow-wrasse** (p. 97)

1.5 scales above lateral line (*Suezichthys*)
6 *Suezichthys aylingi* Russell, 1985 **Crimson Cleaner-wrasse** (p. 99)
7 *Suezichthys caudovittatus* (Steindachner, 1898) **Red Sea Slender-wrasse** (p. 100)
8 *Suezichthys devisi* (Whitley, 1941) **Australian Slender-wrasse** (p. 101)
9 *Suezichthys gracilis* (Steindachner & Döderlein, 1887) **Japanese Slender-wrasse** (p. 100)
10 *Suezichthys soelae* Russell, 1985 **Soela Trawl-wrasse** (p. 101)
11 *Suezichthys* cf *soelae* (Japan) **Japanese Trawl-wrasse** (p.101)

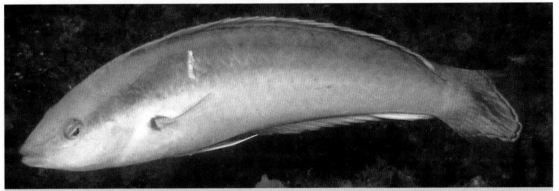

Suezichthys devisi. Male, length 13 cm. Swansea, NSW, Australia. Depth 5 m.

Members of *Suezichthys* occur from Africa and the Red Sea to the Pacific, but are mostly subtropical, and those in tropical waters usually occur in deep water where temperatures are lower. The females of many species are identical, generally plain in colour, except for three black spots in those which have 2.5 scale rows above the lateral line, one on each end of the dorsal fin and one on the caudal fin base. A form that has been named as *Suezichthys tripunctatus* and was also described as *S. russelli*. The validity will probably be decided when the male form becomes known. This similarity and the application of the scientific key to the species (Russell, 1985) has led to numerous erroneous geographical records and those names of earlier described species, such as *S. gracilis* from Japan, have been applied to other species in Australia (*S. devisi*) and Arabian Seas (*S. caudovittatus*). Sibling species are also similar in the gaudy terminal stage and this has led to the same name being used for those between Japan (*S. notatus*) and the Australian - New Zealand region (*S. arquatus*).

Suezichthys-wrasses are small, with most reaching about 14 cm in length and the largest 20 cm. A few species were kept in captivity and proved easy to maintain but most required cooling, as the lost colour when temperatures exceeded about 20°C. Several species occur on muddy substrates and enter harbours where they are found along the edges of deep channels, where tidal currents are strong, and some prefer clearer oceanic conditions where they are found along the edges of rocky reefs bordering rubble and sand. Unlike the 'true' pseudolabrines' these fishes sleep under the sand at night, or dive into it for safety when threatened. When kept in an aquarium, an area of fine sand is essential to keep them happy, especially when dealing with juvenile fish. Gravel or coarse coral sand, if used frequently, usually causes problems. Small juveniles tend to 'disappear', possibly damaging themselves when trying to bury themselves in the sea bed for the night, or adults are unable to apply a slimy 'cocoon' as some species do for protection.

Painted Rainbow-wrasse *Suezichthys arquatus*
Suezichthys arquatus Russell, 1985.
Poor Knight Islands, New Zealand.

Known from southern Queensland, NSW and north-east NZ to Norfolk Island and New Caledonia. Occurs on rocky reefs with low algae and sponge growth in estuaries to very deep offshore where trawled. Males identified by their gaudy colours. Juveniles and females pearly spotted along scale rows with a dark spot at each end of dorsal fin and on base of caudal fin. Length usually to 15 cm, occasionally 16 cm or more when deep.

S. arquatus. Male. Sydney, NSW. D. 15 m. L. 12 cm.

S. arquatus. **B** Male. Montague I., NSW. Depth 15 m. Length 13 cm. **C** Juvenile. Sydney. Depth 6 m. Length 65 mm.

S. arquatus. **D** Male. Southern Qld. Depth 15 m. Length 12 cm. Neville Coleman. **E** Female. Sydney. Depth 6 m. Length 95 mm.

S. arquatus. Male. Swansea, NSW. Depth 12 m. Length 15 cm.

Japan's Rainbow-wrasse *Suezichthys notatus*

Pseudolabrus notatus Kamohara, 1958. Japan.

Known for certain from Japan and possibly Hawaii. Occurs on deep rocky reefs in coastal to offshore waters, usually at depths over 40 m. The name *Suezichthys tripunctatus* has been used for 3-spotted female forms of various species. The male *S. notatus* has been confused with *S. arquatus*, its sibling species from the southern hemisphere. Juveniles and females have a black spot at each end of the dorsal fin and one at upper caudal fin-base.The male retains a distinctive spot heading the dorsal fin. Length to 18 cm, but usually to 15 cm.

A

S. notatus. Female. Izu Oceanic Park, Japan.

B

S. notatus. Ogasawara Islands, Japan. Yasuhiro Morita.

Tristan Rainbow-wrasse *Suezichthys ornatus*

Labrus ornatus Carmichael, 1819. Tristan da Cunha.

Known only from the southern Atlantic island off South Africa. T.C. Andrews *et al*, 1995, reported this species as the most numerous on the shelf areas of the three northern Tristan islands where it inhabits waters from 1.5–50 m depth. It occurs on reefs or in kelp beds and reaches a length of 25 cm.

The colouration of *Suezichthys ornatus* suggests it is a sibling of *S. arquatus* and *S. notatus*. Russell proposed *Nelabrichthys* for this species (1983) but later, in his Pseudolabrine study (1988), suggested this genus to be virtually identical to *Suezichthys,* but it was not mentioned in his *Suezichthys*-revision of the same year.

A

S. ornatus. Female. Tristan. Length 11 cm. T.C. Andrews.

B

S. ornatus. Male. Tristan. L. 20 cm. T.C. Andrews.

Blue-throat Rainbow -wrasse
Suezichthys cyanolaemus

Suezichthys cyanolaemus Russell, 1985.
Rottnest Island, Western Australia.

Known for certain from Rottnest Island to Shark Bay, but may range further north in deep water and records of *Suezichthys notatus* probably are of this species. Rocky reef margins on rubble, and at various depths from shallow protected inlets to deep offshore. Female with black spots on dorsal and caudal-fin base like its close relatives of the *'notatus'*-complex. Length to 12 cm.

S. cyanolaemus. Male. Aquarium, Perth, WA. Length 12 cm.

S. cyanolaemus. Rottnest Island, WA. **B** Male. **C** Female. Barry Hutchins.

Striped Trawl-wrasse
Suezichthys bifurcatus

Suezichthys bifurcatus Russell, 1986.
Great Australian Bight, Western Australia.

Only known from a few specimens from the Great Australian Bight to Rottnest Island. Usually trawled in depths of almost 100 m, but some were photographed on deep rubble near algae reefs. Readily identified by its distinctive colouration. Length to 10 cm.

S. bifurcatus. Rottnest Island, WA. D. 26 m. L. 10 cm. Barry Hutchins.

S. bifurcatus. Aquarium. Specimen from Rottnest Island, WA. Length 10 cm. Barry Hutchins.

Crimson Cleaner-wrasse *Suezichthys aylingi*

Suezichthys aylingi Russell, 1985. Poor Knights, New Zealand.

Eastern Australia from central NSW to Tasmania and off north-eastern New Zealand. Occurs on open coastal reefs and islands, usually along reef-margins bordering onto rubble and sand at about 20 m depth. Juveniles secretive on rubble in gutters or below large rocky overhangs. Adults in loose aggregations and dominated by a large male. Adults are often seen cleaning parasites from large fishes and may rise high above the substrate to meet them. Length to 12 cm.

A

S. aylingi. Male. Montague Island, NSW. Depth 20 m. Length 10 cm.

B

S. aylingi. Bermagui, NSW. Depth 24 m. Length 25 mm.

C

S. aylingi. Male. Bermagui, NSW. Depth 18 m. Length 11 cm.

D

S. aylingi. Seal Rocks, NSW. Depth 12 m. Length 62 mm.

E

S. aylingi. Male. Bermagui, NSW. Depth 20 m. Length 11 cm.

F

S. aylingi. Montague I, NSW. Depth 20 m. Length 8 cm.

H

S. aylingi. Male. Bermagui, NSW. Depth 16 m. Length 12 cm.

G

S. aylingi. Montague I, NSW. Depth 15 m. Length 8 cm.

I

S. aylingi. Male 'cleaning' pike. Bermagui, NSW.

J

S. aylingi. Ile des Phoques, Tasmania. Depth 25 m. Length 11 cm.

A

B

C

Japan's Slender-wrasse *Suezichthys gracilis*

Labrichthys gracilis Steindachner & Döderlein, 1887. Tokyo, Japan.

Southern Japan from Tokyo Bay to sub-tropical waters. Occurs on open sandy and muddy substrates with outcrops of reef or debris, usually at depths of 15 m or more. Easily identified by its colour pattern at all stages, showing a blotched mid-lateral stripe when small and often with pale bars interrupting their darker upper sides as adults. Length to 13 cm.

S. gracilis. Oshima, Japan. Depth 25 m. Length 12 cm.

S. gracilis. Kochi, Japan. **B** Male. Depth 25 m. Length 13 cm. **C** Juvenile. Depth 40 m. Length 25 mm. Tomonori Hirata.

D

E

S. gracilis. Osezaki, Japan. **F** Male. Depth 35 m. Length 13 cm. **G** Female? Depth 25 m. Length 10 cm.

A

Australian slender-wrasse *Suezichthys devisi*

Guntheria devisi Whitley, 1941. Fraser Island, Qld.

Eastern Australia from Capricornia, Qld to Jervis Bay, with expatriates further south, and New Caledonia in the southern Coral Sea. Commonly enters estuaries and harbours where they are found on silty sand or muddy substrates, but also along deeper reefs and sand and rubble in coastal waters to at least 30 m depth. Similar to its Japanese sibling, but has a shorter snout and a distinct axil spot. Length to 14 cm.

B

S. devisi. Sydney, NSW. D. 23 m. Length 38 mm.

S. devisi. Male. Wreck Bay, NSW. Depth 20 m. Length 12 cm.

D

C

S. devisi. **C** Female. Sydney Harbour, NSW. Depth 18 m. Length 10 cm. **D** Coogee, NSW. Depth 9 m. Length 13 cm.

Labrichthys caudavittatus Steindachner, 1898. Suez.

Red Sea and Arabian Seas. Small aggregations of juveniles were seen at 25 m on open sand adjacent to reefs but some adults may prefer deeper water. Living colour of male unknown. Markings similar to *Suezichthys soelae*. Length to 12 cm.

A   **B**

S. caudavittatus. Juveniles. Safaga, Egypt, Red Sea. Depth 25 m. Length 55 mm.

Soela Trawl-wrasse *Suezichthys soelae*

Suezichthys soelae Russell, 1985. North-western Shelf, Australia.

North-west shelf of Western Australia. Occurs on rubble substrates and is known from trawls at a depth of 30–75 m. Closely related to *Suezichthys devisi* and females of *S. soelae* are distinguished from this species by the dark spot heading the dorsal fin. Males are distinguished by their spotted caudal fin. A similar species in Japan. Length to 12 cm.

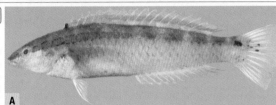

A

B

S. soelae. Dampier Archipelago, WA. **A** Female. D. 32 m. L. 10 cm. **B** Male. D. 57 m. L. 12 cm. CSIRO, Div. of Marine Res. G. Leyland.

Japanese Trawl-wrasse *Suezichthys* cf *soelae*

Suezichthys undescribed.

A little known subtropical species from deep waters in the Okinawa to the Izu-region, southern Japan, that appears to be undescribed. Closely related to *Suezichthys soelae* from Australia. Length to 11 cm.

A

B

S. cf *soelae*. Oshima I., Izu, Japan. **A** Female. D. 42 m. L. 65 mm. **B** Male. D. 50 m. L. 10 cm. Yasuaki Miyamoto.

Most wrasses belong to the subfamily Julininae. They are grouped together because of various characteristics but also are the species that primarily associate with reefs and bury themselves in the sand to sleep. This group also encompasses most of the species that are found in the aquarium trade and in general are easily kept. Most species are small when fully grown and have attractive colouring. A few species grow large and are best kept in public aquariums. They are pelagic spawners, releasing their gametes near the surface. Larvae of some of the species are carried far beyond their normal breeding range.

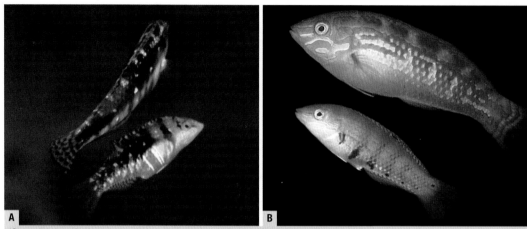

'Spawning jump' was a term used by Tomonori Hirata who photographed **A**, *Halichoeres nebulosus* about to spawn, Kochi, Japan, and seems rather appropriate for when these fishes quickly rise to the surface to spawn and immediately after the release of their gametes rush back to the substrate. **B** *H. schwartzii* a female below and male above leaving the sea bed to spawn at the surface.

A selection of wrasses of the subfamily Julininae. The 'Ear-spot' *Macropharyngodon kuiteri*, the orange-band *Halichoeres hartzfeldii* and the blue-tailed *Anampses femininus* get along well in the author's aquarium. Collected in the Sydney, Australia, region and all were grown from tiny juveniles to adults. They were raised on a diet of scallops and meat, finely chopped, mysids, mosquito larvae and *Galeolaria*-worms that are shown in the foreground. The latter occur commonly in colonies in tidal zones on rocks or jetty pylons.

Parajulis 104

Leptojulis 105

Halichoeres (Indo-Pacific) 108

Macropharyngodon 141

Xenojulis 148

Ophthalmolepis 149

Coris 150

Hologymnosus 170

Pseudocoris 174

PSEUDOJULOIDES 179

Anampses 186

STETHOJULIS 197

HEMIGYMNUS 204

Feminine. Type species: *Julis poecilepterus* Temminck & Schlegel, 1845. A monotypic genus from China seas to the major islands of southern Japan. Closely related to *Leptojulis*.

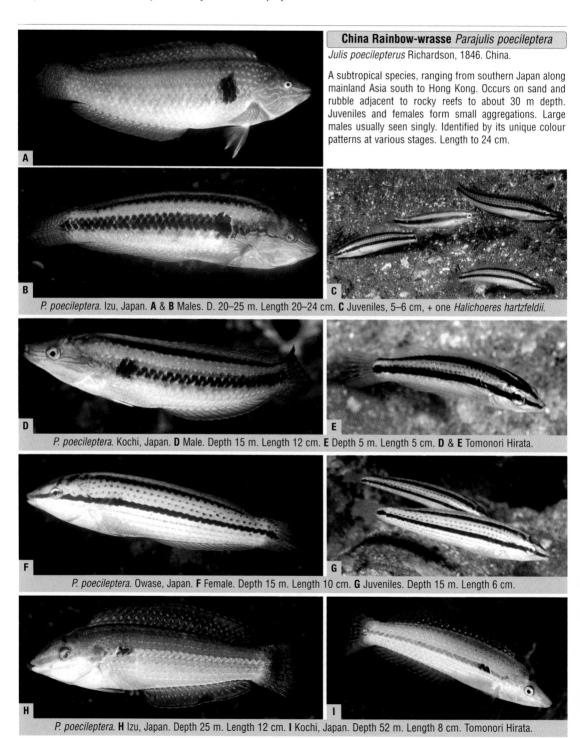

China Rainbow-wrasse *Parajulis poecileptera*

Julis poecilepterus Richardson, 1846. China.

A subtropical species, ranging from southern Japan along mainland Asia south to Hong Kong. Occurs on sand and rubble adjacent to rocky reefs to about 30 m depth. Juveniles and females form small aggregations. Large males usually seen singly. Identified by its unique colour patterns at various stages. Length to 24 cm.

P. poecileptera. Izu, Japan. **A** & **B** Males. D. 20–25 m. Length 20–24 cm. **C** Juveniles, 5–6 cm, + one *Halichoeres hartzfeldii*.

P. poecileptera. Kochi, Japan. **D** Male. Depth 15 m. Length 12 cm. **E** Depth 5 m. Length 5 cm. **D** & **E** Tomonori Hirata.

P. poecileptera. Owase, Japan. **F** Female. Depth 15 m. Length 10 cm. **G** Juveniles. Depth 15 m. Length 6 cm.

P. poecileptera. **H** Izu, Japan. Depth 25 m. Length 12 cm. **I** Kochi, Japan. Depth 52 m. Length 8 cm. Tomonori Hirata.

Feminine. Type species: *Julis (Halichoeres) cyanopleura* Bleeker, 1853. A small Indo-Pacific genus with 5 species. Most species have a restricted distribution and are rarely encountered.

    1 *Leptojulis chrysotaenia* Randall & Ferraris, 1981 **Ochre-band Wrasse** (p. 107)
    2 *Leptojulis cyanopleura* (Bleeker, 1853) **Blue-spot Wrasse** (p. 106)
    3 *Leptojulis lambdastigma* Randall & Ferraris, 1981 **Trawl V-Wrasse** (N.A.)
    4 *Leptojulis polylepis* Randall, 1996 **Black-spot V-wrasse** (p. 107)
    5 *Leptojulis urostigma* Randall, 1996 **Tail-spot V-wrasse** (p. 107)

The species of *Leptojulis* share an unusually shaped marking on top of the head when adult, which, when seen from above, looks like a 'V' or 'Y', and is situated just ahead of the dorsal fin. Such a mark is present in *Parajulis* but not as obvious. The two genera are similar to *Halichoeres* but differ in teeth arrangement in the jaws and in the structure of sensory pores such as in the lateral-line and on the head. Some other wrasse-species presently assigned to *Halichoeres* are similar to members of *Leptojulis* and some juvenile *Halichoeres* may be confused with *Leptojulis* when using scientific keys. The genera are often seen mixed when juveniles form small aggregations.

Most species of *Leptojulis* live on deep slopes or flats of mixed substrates with sand and rubble, sparse invertebrate cover, and often in silty habitats. Only *L. cyanopleura* is commonly observed on shallow reefs and is best known. Juveniles form small groups and feed on zooplankton. With growth they rise higher above the substrate and are often seen swimming with other similarly sized planktivores such as *Cirrhilabrus*-wrasses in tropical waters. In the Sydney region this species is a tropical expatriate where it mixes with hulafishes, a small plesiopid fish that forms large schools near reefs.

This species is easily kept and grows within about 6 months to adult size. It is unlikely that the other members of the genus are as easy and will probably not appear for sale very often. They can be kept with other planktivorous fishes and are suitable for the invertebrate aquarium. Some open swimming space is much liked by these fishes and sand to bury themselves in at night is essential, especially for juveniles.

Leptojulis cyanopleura. Type-species for the genus. Bali, Indonesia. Male. Depth 6 m. Length 12 cm.

A

Blue-spot V-wrasse *Leptojulis cyanopleura*

Julis (Halichoeres) cyanopleura Bleeker, 1853. Java.

Widespread Indo-West Pacific, ranging to subtropical zones. Clear coastal slopes to outer reef lagoons on open rubble patches or rocky sea beds. Occurs in small aggregations of mostly females. Slender species, usually with brown or dusky mid-lateral stripe. Male with reflective blue spot in the dark band, just past and above the pectoral fin. Length to 12 cm.

L. cyanopleura. Male. Bali, Indonesia. Depth 6 m. Length 12 cm.

B

C

L. cyanopleura. Male. Maldives. Depth 25 m. Length 12 cm.

L. cyanopleura. Male. Bali, Indonesia. D. 6 m. L. 12 cm.

D

E

L. cyanopleura. **D** Young male. Sydney, Australia. Depth 7 m. Length 8 cm. **E** Male. Flores, Indonesia. Depth 10 m. Length 10 cm.

F

G

L. cyanopleura. Sydney, Australia. **F** Female. Depth 7 m. Length 6 cm. **G** Juvenile. Depth 4 m. Length 35 mm.

H

I

L. cyanopleura. **H** Females with *Trachinops*. Sydney, Australia. D. 7 m. L. 7 cm. **I** Juveniles. Bali, Indonesia. D. 24 m. L. 25 mm.

Black-spot V-wrasse *Leptojulis polylepis*

Leptojulis polylepis Randall, 1996. Solomon Islands.

Only known from southern Indonesia, Bali to Flores, and from New Guinea and The Solomon Islands. Coastal slopes, usually in muddy habitats with sparse reef formation, inhabiting the open areas. A slender finely-scaled species with a distinct small black spot on its side, at eye level, just past the pectoral fin. Reported to 46 m depth. Length to 10 cm.

L. polylepis. Male. Flores, Indonesia. Depth 15 m. Length 85 mm.

L. polylepis. Bali, Indonesia. Depth 25 m. **B** Length 35 mm. **C** Length 65 mm.

Tail-spot V-wrasse *Leptojulis urostigma*

Leptojulis urostigma Randall, 1996. Solomon Islands.

Widespread Indonesia to Philippines. Mainly found on open muddy substrates, often deep in front of river mouths where land debris is scattered over the sea bed. Adults were all seen at about 30 m depth and usually swim fast near the bottom. Length to 11 cm.

L. urostigma. Bali. D. 25 m. L. 35 mm.
L. urostigma. **A-C** Males. Maumere, Flores. Depth 30 m. Length 11 cm.

Ochre-band Wrasse *Leptojulis chrysotaenia*

Leptojulis chrysotaenia Randall & Ferraris, 1981. Thailand.

Andaman Sea, ranging east to Bali at least, easily overlooked. Occurs on coastal sand slopes with sparse reef at about 20-30 m depth. Juveniles in small groups. Adults only seen singly. Juveniles are distinguished from other single band species by the ocellus in the dorsal fin and adults by the angled bar on the snout and cheek. A small species, to about 10 cm.

L. chrysotaenia. Male. Sunda Strait. Depth 20 m. Length 8 cm.

L. chrysotaenia. Tulamben, Bali. **B** Depth 15 m. Length 35 mm. **C** Male. Depth 25 m. Length 9 cm.

Masculine. Type species: *Halichoeres bimaculatus* Rüppell, 1835, (= *Julis zeylonicus*). The largest wrasses genus as recently defined, but consists of several distinct groups and further studies will no doubt split these groups into a number of different genera in the way proposed by Bleeker over 150 years ago. In all, there are over 75 species, 54+ of which occur in the Indo-West Pacific and another 20 species in the eastern Pacific and Atlantic waters.

1 *Halichoeres argus* (Bloch & Schneider, 1801) (p. **122**)
2 *Halichoeres bicolor* (Bloch & Schneider, 1801) (p. **113**)
3 *Halichoeres binotopsis* Bleeker, 1849 (p. **117**)
4 *Halichoeres biocellatus* Schultz, 1960 (p. **125**)
5 *Halichoeres brownfieldi* (Whitley, 1945) (p. **123**)
6 *Halichoeres chlorocephalus* Kuiter & Randall, 1995 (p. **120**)
7 *Halichoeres chloropterus* (Bloch, 1791) (p. **140**)
8 *Halichoeres chrysotaenia* Bleeker, 1853 (p. **119**)
9 *Halichoeres chrysus* Randall, 1980 (p. **135**)
10 *Halichoeres cosmetus* Randall & Smith, 1982 (p. **126**)
11 *Halichoeres dussumieri* (Bloch & Schneider 1801) (p. **114**)
12 *Halichoeres exornatus* (Richardson, 1846) (p. **115**)
13 *Halichoeres hartzfeldi* Bleeker, 1852 (p. **110**)
14 *Halichoeres hortulanus* (Lacepède, 1801) (p. **139**)
15 *Halichoeres iridis* Randall & Smith, 1982 (p. **134**)
16 *Halichoeres javanicus* Bleeker, 1857 (p. **115**)
17 *Halichoeres kallochroma* Bleeker, 1853 (p. **119**)
18 *Halichoeres kneri* Bleeker, 1862 (p. **112**)
19 *Halichoeres lamarii* (Valenciennes, 1839) (p. **132**)
20 *Halichoeres lapillus* Smith, 1947 (p. **127**)
21 *Halichoeres leptotaenia* Randall & Earle, 1994 (N.A.)
22 *Halichoeres leucoxanthus* Randall & Smith, 1982 (p. **135**)
23 *Halichoeres leucurus* (Walbaum, 1792) (p. **120**)
24 *Halichoeres margaritaceus* (Valenciennes, 1839) (p. **128**)
25 *Halichoeres marginatus* Rüppell, 1835 (p. **132**)
26 *Halichoeres melanochir* Fowler & Bean, 1928 (p. **131**)
27 *Halichoeres melanurus* Bleeker, 1851 (p. **118**)
28 *Halichoeres melas* Randall & Earle, 1994 (N.A.)
29 *Halichoeres miniatus* (Valenciennes, 1839) (p. **130**)
30 *Halichoeres nebulosus* (Valenciennes, 1839) (p. **129**)
31 *Halichoeres nigrescens* (Bloch & Schneider 1801) (p. **114**)
32 *Halichoeres orientalis* Randall, 1999 (p. **127**)
33 *Halichoeres ornatissimus* Garrett, 1864 (p. **126**)
34 *Halichoeres* cf *ornatissimus* (p. **126**)
35 *Halichoeres pallidus* Kuiter & Randall, 1995 (p. **137**)
36 *Halichoeres papillionaceus* (Valenciennes, 1839) (N.A.)
37 *Halichoeres pardaleocephalus* Bleeker, 1849 (N.A.)
38 *Halichoeres pelicieri* Randall & Smith, 1982 (p. **110**)
39 *Halichoeres podostigma* Bleeker, 1854 (p. **140**)
40 *Halichoeres prosopeion* Bleeker, 1853 (p. **138**)
41 *Halichoeres richmondi* Fowler & Bean, 1928 (p. **122**)
42 *Halichoeres rubricephalus* Kuiter & Randall, 1995 (p. **121**)
43 *Halichoeres scapularis* (Bennett, 1831) (p. **112**)
44 *Halichoeres schwartzii* Bleeker, 1849 (p. **116**)
45 *Halichoeres signifer* Randall & Earle, 1994 (N.A.)
46 *Halichoeres solorensis* Bleeker, 1853 (p. **134**)
47 *Halichoeres stigmaticus* Randall & Smith, 1982 (N.A.)
48 *Halichoeres tenuispinis* (Günther, 1862) (p. **124**)
49 *Halichoeres timorensis* Bleeker, 1852 (p. **117**)
50 *Halichoeres tremebundus* Jordan & Snyder, 1902 (p. **124**)
51 *Halichoeres trimaculatus* (Quoy & Gaimard, 1834) (p. **113**)
52 *Halichoeres trispilus* Randall & Smith, 1982 (p. **137**)
53 *Halichoeres xanti* (Karoli, 1882) (p. **136**)
54 *Halichoeres zeylonicus* (Bennett, 1832) (p. **111**)

The Indo-Pacific members of the genus *Halichoeres* are mostly distributed in tropical waters, a few ranging to sub-temperate zones. They feature large cycloid scales on the body that extend as much smaller ones over the nape and thorax, and a single lateral line with an abrupt bend below the end of the soft dorsal fin. The head is mostly naked but some species have a few small scales on the opercle. The mouth is relatively small and the jaws have a single row of conical teeth that are progressively larger at the front. They sometimes have enlarged canines in the upper jaw at the corners of the mouth, but sometimes this is an adult or male feature. The diagnosis for the genus is presently rather broad and needs to be refined to determine what various groups, subgenera or actual valid genera lie within.

On tropical reefs there are usually several species of *Halichoeres* present, some sharing habitats and others having a particular preference. The species inhabits estuaries and shallow harbours, reef flats, walls and sand-flats, but always near sand or rubble in which they bury themselves to sleep at night. Habitats range from intertidal algae and rock, seagrass beds to deep sponge beds or rubble slopes at the base of deep drop-offs. Juveniles and adults are usually found in the same habitats. They feed primarily on small invertebrates, crustaceans and worms, but larval or tiny juvenile fishes may be taken as well. Whilst usually seeking food from the substrate, when zooplankton is available the schooling species will take to it and may feed high above the sea bed. Colours vary with habitat and most of the shallow water species have camouflage colours that blend with algae backgrounds. Different species that live in the same habitats may have near identical colours and can be difficult to identify. Usually the males are distinguished by differences in colour patterns on the head or fins, and sometimes show very different colours during courtship displays.

Halichoeres zeylonicus.
Type-species for genus and subgenus *Halichoeres*

Halichoeres scapularis.
Type-species for subgenus. *Guentheria.*

Halichoeres hortulanus.
Type-species for subgenus *Hemitautoga*

Halichoeres miniatus.
Type-species for subgenus. *Platyglossus.*

Halichoeres brownfieldi.
Belongs to the *brownfieldi-tenuispinus* group

Halichoeres argus.
Type-species for subgenus. *Hemiulis.*

Deep-water species are generally plainer but more colourful, and are usually easily identified.

Most of the species that are placed in the genus *Halichoeres* do well in captivity, but the genus comprises several different groups that may belong in different genera and may require different care. Many are beautifully coloured and most do not grow large, thus making them ideal for the home aquarium. The 'true' *Halichoeres* are those such as *H. zeylonicus, hartzfeldii* or *pelicieri* which live on open substrates where they often roam in large groups, whilst some others are more reef-bound. Those species living on open substrates usually do much better in large aquariums that have large sand and rubble areas than in small ones crowded with reef formations in which one should keep to the reef-dwellers, and preferably smaller species. All require some sand to sleep in although large adults of some species may find a spot amongst rocks.

A mixture of species can be kept and they are also suited to the community or display aquarium. However, they are not well suited to the invertebrate aquarium and will usually eat worms or small crustaceans and probably kill others. Tiny juveniles are easily grown and ideal to begin with, especially if a few different species can be obtained. They grow quickly and reach full size in one or two years. Many species have been kept for 5–7 years but no doubt some can live much longer.

Pelicier's Wrasse *Halichoeres pelicieri*

Halichoeres pelicieri Randall & Smith, 1982. Mauritius.

Mauritius. Occurs on sand and rubble adjacent to reefs at moderate depths from about 20 m. A male was caught on a line at 85 m by Daniel Pelicier, after whom the fish was named. This species is similar to *Halichoeres zeylonicus*, but males have a mostly black dorsal fin. Length to 16 cm.

H. pelicieri. Mauritius. Jerry Allen.

Orange-line Wrasse *Halichoeres hartzfeldii*

Julis (Halichoeres) hartzfeldii Bleeker, 1852. Ambon I.

Widespread West Pacific, ranging west to Bali. Replaced by *H. zeylonicus* further west. Coastal and inner reefs on adjacent sand slopes, deep lagoons and harbours or flats with rubble or bommies. Adults usually in small groups of females and males moving over large areas by themselves, regularly checking females. Juveniles in small to large aggregations. Length usually to 16 cm, but can reach 20 cm.

H. hartzfeldii. Male. Qld, Australia. Depth 12 m. Length 13.5 cm.

H. hartzfeldii. **B** Male. Bali, Indonesia. Depth 6 m. Length 16 cm. **C** Sydney, Australia. Depth 15 m. Length 25 mm.

H. hartzfeldii. Kochi, Japan. **D** Male, nuptial. Depth 16 m. Length 12 cm. **E** Depth 20 m. Length 40 mm. **D** & **E** Tomonori Hirata.

H. hartzfeldii. Kochi, Japan. **F** Male. Depth 16 m. Length 12 cm. Tomonori Hirata. **G** Female. Bali, Indonesia. Depth 6 m. L. 14 cm.

H. *hartzfeldii*. NSW, Australia. **H & I** Sydney. Depth 12 m. Length 7 & 10 cm. **J** Montague Island, Depth 20 m. Lengths 35–50 mm. *Halichoeres hartzfeldii* and its sibling *H. zeylonicus* form small to large aggregations on sandy substrates from postlarval stage on. The largest individual becomes the male that dominates and defends the group. If it dies, the next largest changes sex to take over this role.

Sri Lankan Wrasse *Halichoeres zeylonicus*

Julis zeylonicus Bennett, 1833. Sri Lanka.

Widespread Indian Ocean, ranging east to the north coast of Bali where it co-occurs with its Pacific sibling *Halichoeres hartzfeldii*. The two species have similar colour patterns but differences are best seen between males with their different cheek patterns and in the way the mid-lateral stripe is interrupted by a dark or orange bar, although the mid-lateral stripe is considerably thinner in the female and juvenile stages of *H. zeylonicus*. Occurs on open sand slopes or deep sand-flats between reefs. Usually in small groups of females with single males patrolling the area. Appears to be a slightly smaller species than *H. hartzfeldii* with largest specimens having a length of about 15 cm.

H. zeylonicus. Male. Maldives. Depth 25 m. Length 15 cm.

H. zeylonicus. Male. Tulamben, Bali. Depth 25 m. Length 15 cm.

H. zeylonicus. Females. **C** Maldives. Depth 25 m. Length 12 cm. **D** Pulau Putri, Java. Depth 15 m. Length 12 cm.

111

A

H. scapularis. Male. Bali, Indonesia. Depth 6 m. Length 15 cm.

Zigzag Wrasse *Halichoeres scapularis*

Julis scapularis Bennett, 1832. Mauritius.

Widespread Indo West Pacific. Occurs on sand and rubble near or amongst reefs, lagoons and estuaries. Adults to about 30 m depth. Juveniles pale with black mid-lateral line, zig-zagging over scale-edges. Males lose this black stripe or it is reduced to a short dash and becomes part of the ornamental pattern. Length to 15 cm.

B

C

H. scapularis. **B** Male. Bali, Indonesia. Depth 6 m. Length 15 cm. **C** Kochi, Japan. Depth 20 m. Length 35 mm. Tomonori Hirata.

D

E

H. scapularis. Kochi, Japan. **D** Female. Depth 5 m. Length 12 cm. **E** Depth 5 m. Length 8 cm. **D** & **E** Tomonori Hirata.

A

H. kneri. Male. Tejakula, Bali. Depth 3 m. Length 10 cm.

Kner's Wrasse *Halichoeres kneri*

Halichoeres kneri Bleeker, 1862. Java.

Widespread West Pacific, Java and Singapore to Bali and southern Japan, and south to eastern Australia. Sometimes co-occurs with the similar *Halichoeres nigrescens*. Shallow inshore waters, usually in silty habitats on rocky reefs or on sand adjacent to reefs. Juveniles and females with thick mid-lateral stripe and ocellus midway in dorsal fin. Latter fades to small spot in males. Length to 10 cm.

B

C

H. kneri. **B** Female. Tejakula, Bali. Depth 3 m. Length 7 cm. **C** Ehime, Japan. D. 4 m. Length 40 mm. Tomonori Hirata.

Three-spot Wrasse *Halichoeres trimaculatus*

Julis trimaculata Quoy & Gaimard, 1834. SW Pacific.

Widespread West Pacific. Occurs on sand and rubble near or amongst reefs and in lagoons. Juveniles in shallow water on rubble in protected coastal waters. Adults to about 30 m depth. Usually a pale looking species with a black spot on tail base that is large in adults. Males more colourful with pink and yellow. Length to 20 cm.

H. trimaculatus. Male. Flores, Indonesia. Depth 20 m. Length 18 cm.

B

H. trimaculatus. Qld, Australia. D. 6 m. L. 45 mm.

C

D

H. trimaculatus. Kochi, Japan. **C** Female. Depth 8 m. Length 10 cm. **D** Depth 5 m. Length 15 cm. **C** & **D** Tomonori Hirata.

Pearly-spotted Wrasse *Halichoeres bicolor*

Labrus bicolor Bloch & Schneider, 1801. No locality.

Andaman Sea to Java. Inshore, usually in silty habitats on sand or mud near shallow reefs and seagrass beds. Mid-lateral stripe is thin when young, but widens to about eye-diameter width when adult, with a series of pearly blue spots running along the centre. Black spot between 6th and 7th dorsal fin spines in initial phase, usually faded in large males. To about 20 m depth. Length to 12 cm.

A

H. bicolor. Male. Singapore. Depth 15 m. Length 12 cm.

B

C

H. bicolor. **B** Singapore. Depth 15 m. Length 7 cm. **C** Male. Singapore. Depth 15 m. Length 10 cm.

D

E

H. bicolor. Pulau Putri, Java. **D** Depth 10 m. Length 7 cm. **E** Depth 10 m. Length 9 cm.

White-button Wrasse *Halichoeres nigrescens*

Labrus nigrescens Bloch & Schneider, 1801. No locality*.

Indo-West Pacific, uncertain distribution as part of a widespread species-complex. The males and females of *Halichoeres nigrescens* have a bluish black spot from 5th to 7th dorsal spines. It occurs throughout tropical Australian coastal waters and probably ranges to south-eastern Indonesia and New Guinea. It inhabits algae reefs in sheltered bays, usually in a few metres depth. Length to 14 cm in WA.

*The same year they also described *Coris picta,* which is endemic to Australia, and gave for *Halichoeres argus* the type locality as 'New Holland' = Australia. It is likely that this type of *H. nigrescens* came from Australia, especially since it occurs in the same habitat as *H. argus.*

A

H. nigrescens. Male. Qld, Australia. Depth 7 m. Length 75 mm.

B

H. nigrescens. Female. Qld, Australia. Length 7 cm. Roger Steene.

C

H. nigrescens. Dampier, WA. D. 2 m. L. 14 cm. Jerry Allen.

Dussumier's Wrasse *Halichoeres dussumieri*

Julis dussumieri Valenciennes, 1839. India.

Widespread Indian Ocean in continental coastal waters, ranging east to Bali. Usually found in sheltered inshore algae-rocky habitats at a depth of a few metres. Identified by cheek pattern, and some males have a small bluish spot on the spinous dorsal between 5th and 7th spine. Young and females have 3 rows of yellowish spots in the dorsal fin and lack a black spot. Length to 16 cm.

A

H. dussumieri. Male. Bali, Indonesia. Depth 2 m. Length 16 cm.

B

H. dussumieri. Male. Bali, Indonesia. Depth 2 m. Length 16 cm.

C

H. dussumieri. Java, Indonesia. Depth 1 m. Length 8 cm.

D

E

H. dussumieri. Java, Indonesia. **D** Depth 3 m. Length 15 cm. **C** Depth 4 m. Length 12 cm.

Java Wrasse *Halichoeres javanicus*

Halichoeres javanicus Bleeker, 1862. Java.

Only known from Java and Singapore regions. Records from Hong Kong are based on *Halichoeres exornatus*. It occurs on mixed algae and coral reefs in sheltered bays, often silty, to about 15 m depth. Small juveniles have a small black peduncular spot. Adults have a shiny black to blue-green spot on the dorsal fin at the 6th and 7th spine. The general pattern consists primarily of longitudinal lines, but sometimes with faint barring and small black spots. Length to 12 cm.

A

H. javanicus. Male. Singapore. Depth 12 m. Length 12 cm.

B

H. javanicus. Pulau Putri. Depth 4 m. Length 4 cm.

C

H. javanicus. Male. Singapore. Depth 8 m. Length 12 cm.

D

H. javanicus. Singapore. Depth 8 m. Length 9 cm.

E

F

H. javanicus. Female. Pulau Putri. Depth 4 m. Length 7 cm.

Hong Kong Wrasse *Halichoeres exornatus*

Halichoeres exornatus Richardson, 1846. Hong Kong.

Hong Kong and adjacent tropical waters to the Philippines and south to Borneo. Previously confused with *Halichoeres javanicus*. The male has a distinctive head-pattern with mostly horizontal lines. A reef dweller in sheltered habitats to about 10 m depth. Length to 16 cm.

A

B

H. exornatus. **A** Female. Philippines. Depth 4 m. Length 12 cm. **B** Male. N. Borneo, Malaysia. D. 5 m. L. 16 cm. **A** & **B** Jerry Allen.

115

Julis (Halichoeres) schwartzii Bleeker, 1847. Bali.
?Julis papillionaceus Valenciennes, 1839.
Santa Cruz Islands, sw Pacific.

Flores and Banda Sea, ranging west to Bali. Doubtfully the same as *H. papillionaceus* from the Pacific. The included species is what Bleeker described. Occurs only on very shallow reef flats, sub-tidal or in lagoons with seagrasses, usually at less than 2 m depth. Males are identified by their cheek patterns and unusual dorsal fin shape (**F**). Generally green in seagrasses and more grey on algae reef flats. Length to 10 cm.

H. schwartzii. Male, displaying to female. Flores, Indonesia. D. 1 m. L. 10 cm.

H. schwartzii. Bali, Indonesia. **B** Male. Depth 0.5 m. Length 10 cm. **C** Depth 0.5 m. Length 65 mm.

H. schwartzii. Indonesia. **D** Female. Bali. Depth 0.5 m. Length 85 mm. **E** Flores. Depth 1 m. Length 65 mm.

H. schwartzii. Male. Flores, Indonesia. Depth 1 m.

Saowisata Wrasse *Halichoeres binotopsis*

Julis (Halichoeres) binotopsis Bleeker, 1849. Bali.

Southern Indonesia, known from Bali to Flores. Shallow coastal reef flats and gutters with algae and sparse coral growth. Occurs in small loose aggregations. Males territorial with numerous females spread over a section of reef. Similar to *H. timorensis* (next species) and best distinguished by the more horizontal line pattern on the cheek. Length to 12 cm.

A

H. binotopsis. Male. Flores, Indonesia. Depth 2 m. Length 12 cm.

B

C

H. binotopsis. Flores, Indonesia. **B** Depth 2 m. Length 45 mm. **C** Female. Depth 2 m. Length 12 cm.

Timor Wrasse *Halichoeres timorensis*

Julis (Halichoeres) timorensis Bleeker, 1852. Timor.

Widespread Indonesia and Andaman Sea to Sri Lanka. Shallow coastal reefs, mainly rock substrates with soft coral and algae growth. Identified by cheek and body patterns. Most similar to *H. binotopsis* (above) and is best distinguished by the more angular versus horizontal cheek lines. Occurs in small loose groups dominated by a large male. Length to 12 cm.

A

H. timorensis. Male. Sulawesi, Indonesia. Depth 3 m. Length 12 cm.

B

C

H. timorensis. Indonesia. **B** Tulamben. D. 3 m. L. 10 cm. **C** Sumba. Male. Length 12 cm. Takamasa Tonozuka.

D

E

H. timorensis. Indonesia. **D** Sunda Strait, Java. Depth 15 m. Length 9 cm. **E** Female. Sulawesi. Depth 3 m. Length 10 cm.

Hoeven's Wrasse *Halichoeres melanurus*

Julis (Halichoeres) melanurus Bleeker, 1851. Banda.
Julis (Halichoeres) hoevenii Bleeker, 1851. Banda.

Widespread West Pacific, but distinct geographical forms, and replaced by Indian Ocean sibling west of Bali. Various shallow protected reef habitats, but mainly inshore. Several other similar *Halichoeres* species in which females are difficult to distinguish from each other with near identical colour patterns. Males differ in various ways most obviously in the fins, such as lines versus spots. This species has lines on the caudal fin, usually ending in black, forming a spot when fin is compressed. Length to 12 cm.

H. melanurus. Male. Bali, Indonesia. Depth 5 m. Length 12 cm.

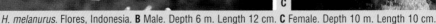

H. melanurus. Flores, Indonesia. **B** Male. Depth 6 m. Length 12 cm. **C** Female. Depth 10 m. Length 10 cm.

H. melanurus (var 1). Kochi, Japan. **D** Male. Depth 5 m. Length 8 cm. **E** Female. Depth 7 m. Length 7 cm. Tomonori Hirata.

H. melanurus (var 2). Qld, Australia. Depth 5–10 m. **F** & **H** Males. **G** Female. L. 6 cm. **I** Changing sex. L. 9 cm.

Vrolik's Wrasse *Halichoeres chrysotaenia*

Julis (Halichoeres) chrysotaenia Bleeker, 1853. Java.
Julis (Halichoeres) vrolikii Bleeker, 1855. Batu Island.

Java and Andaman Sea, ranging to the Maldives. Originally described from the Jakarta region where *H. melanurus* is absent and this species is common. It occurs on shallow protected reefs or in lagoons with good coral growth, to about 20 m depth. Males are distinguished from *H. melanurus* by their spotted caudal fin, whilst females appear to have finer lines along the body. Length to 12 cm.

A

H. chrysotaenia. Male. Java, Indonesia. Depth 5 m. Length 12 cm.

B

C

H. chrysotaenia. Java, Indonesia. **B** Female. Depth 5 m. Length 9 cm. **C** Male. Depth 8 m. Length 10 cm.

D

E

H. chrysotaenia. Maldives. **D** Female. Depth 5 m. Length 8 cm. **E** Male. Depth 6 m. Length 12 cm.

Pink-snout Wrasse *Halichoeres kallochroma*

Julis (Halichoeres) kallochroma Bleeker, 1853. Pariaman, Sumatra.

Indian Ocean species, known from Sumatra to eastern Andaman sea. Occurs on rubble-algae reef flats and in seagrass habitats. Very similar to *H. leucurus* and at some stage was thought to be the same. The male has a lined body pattern and a tail with numerous thin lines across it. The female is almost identical to *H. leucurus* but has a white spot below the ocellus on the caudal fin base that is only shown in juveniles of *H. leucurus*, and yellowish lips. Length to just over 12 cm.

A

H. kallochroma. Male. Sumatra. D. 10 m. L. 12 cm. H. Debelius.

B

H. kallochroma. Female. Sumatra. D. 10 m. L. 8 cm. H. Debelius.

Grey-head Wrasse *Halichoeres leucurus*

Labrus leucurus Walbaum, 1792. No locality.
Labrus purpurescens Bloch & Schneider, 1801.

Widespread West Pacific, ranging west to Java. Replaced by similar *H. kallochroma* in Sumatra and Andaman sea. Protected coastal reef slopes on mixed coral and algae habitats. Males recognised by their grey-looking head when seen in natural light. Body with lined pattern until female stage. Head of males usually grey with blue lines, but Australian males (**B**) have an inverted pattern of green and orange. Length to 15 cm.

A

H. leucurus. Male. Flores, Indonesia. Depth 10 m. Length 15 cm.

B

H. leucurus? Male. Cassini Reef, WA. D. 10 m. L. 14 cm. J. Allen.

C

H. leucurus. Female. Flores, Indonesia. D. 6 m. L. 12 cm.

D

H. leucurus. Female. Java, Indonesia. D. 6 m. L. 12 cm.

E

H. leucurus. Java, Indonesia. D. 6 m. L. 45 mm.

Green-head Wrasse *Halichoeres chlorocephalus*

Halichoeres chlorocephalus Kuiter & Randall, 1995.

Only known from south-eastern Papua New Guinea. Occurs at moderate depths of about 25 m or more in deep lagoons, harbours and protected bays on soft sea beds with sponges and brittle corals. Juveniles bluish with thin orange lines and yellow snout. Males mostly dark with a green-looking head. Length to 12 cm.

A

B

H. chlorocephalus. New Britain, PNG. **A** Male. Depth 25 m. Length 12 cm. **B** Female. Depth 25 m. Length 65 mm. Jerry Allen.

120

Red-head Wrasse *Halichoeres rubricephalus*

Halichoeres rubricephalus Kuiter & Randall, 1995.
Flores, Indonesia.

Known from Maumere Bay, Flores, and the Banggai Islands. Habitat comprises brittle corals growing dense and high on rubble slopes of inner reefs, at depths of between 10-35 m. Males are identified by their bright red head, even at depths where colour is greatly suppressed. The female is easily mistaken for other orange striped species, but has an additional ocelli at the end of the dorsal fin. Length to about 10 cm.

A

H. rubricephalus. Male. Flores, Indonesia. Depth 25 m. Length 10 cm.

B

H. rubricephalus. Video, Banggai Is. Koji Ozaki.

C

H. rubricephalus. Male. Flores, Indonesia. Depth 25 m. Length 10 cm.

D

E

H. rubricephalus. Females. Flores, Indonesia. Depth 25 m. **C** Length 65 mm. **D** Length 85 mm.

Orange-head Wrasse *Halichoeres* sp 1

Undetermined species, probably new.

Only known from the photograph that was taken in the Philippines. Closely related to *Halichoeres chlorocephalus* and *H. rubricephalus* that both have a limited distribution. This species is probably restricted to the Philippines region. Like its siblings it is found on invertebrate-rich reefs at moderate depths. Length to about 11 cm.

H. sp. Male. Philippines. Depth 20 m. Length 10 cm. Jerry Allen.

A

H. richmondi. Male. Flores, Indonesia. Depth 6 m. Length 14 cm.

Chain-lined Wrasse *Halichoeres richmondi*

Halichoeres richmondi Fowler & Bean, 1928.
Philippines.

Widespread Indonesia to Philippines. Shallow coastal reef crests and slopes with rich soft-coral growth. Occurs in small loose groups. Males are recognised by their orange-brown head and the blue lines that run chain-like along the body. Juveniles and females have an orange to yellow anal fin. The snout is more pointed compared to similar species. Length to 14 cm.

B

H. richmondi. Male. Sulawesi, Indonesia. Depth 9 m. Length 12 cm.

C

H. richmondi. Female. Java, Indonesia. D. 7 m. L. 45 mm.

D

H. richmondi. Female. Flores, Indonesia. Depth 6 m. Length 10 cm.

E

H. richmondi. Female. Java, Indonesia. D. 10 m. L. 95 mm.

A

H. argus. Male. Java. Indonesia. Depth 2 m. Length 10 cm.

Peacock Wrasse *Halichoeres argus*

Labrus argus Bloch & Schneider, 1801, New Holland.

Widespread West Pacific. Coastal, shallow and usually algae-rocky reef flats, in lagoons and seagrasses. Young are bright green when in seagrasses and greenish brown on reefs. Recognised by the unusual colour patterns on the cheek or the black spotted scales over the back. Length to 12 cm.

C

H. argus. Bali, Indonesia. D. 1 m. L. 35 mm.

B

H. argus. Female. Flores, Indonesia. Depth 3 m. Length 12 cm.

D

H. argus. Flores, Indonesia. D. 1 m. L. 65 mm.

Brownfield's Wrasse *Halichoeres brownfieldi*

Choerojulis brownfieldi Whitley, 1945. Western Australia.

Only found in the south-western corner of Western Australia. Occurs on weedy rocky reefs at various depths and juveniles are often seen in small groups amongst *Zostera* seagrasses. Adults swim in small, mixed sex groups, sometimes in separate aggregations of males or females. Juveniles with a double ocellus in the dorsal fin. Usually bright green along upper half of the body. Males lose ocelli, and the white band along their lower side often has a red stripe along its upper edge. Length to 15 cm.

A

H. brownfieldi. Male. Lucky Bay, WA. Depth 20 m. Length 15 cm.

B

C

H. brownfieldi. Lucky Bay, WA. **B** Juvenile. Depth 8 m. Length 35 mm. **C** Female. Depth 20 m. Length 9 cm.

D

E

H. brownfieldi. Lucky Bay, WA. **D** Juveniles. Depth 12 m. Length 65 mm. **E** Male. Depth 12 m. Length 12 cm.

F

H. brownfieldi. Lucky Bay, WA. Males together. Depth 12 m. Length 10–13 cm.

123

Platyglossus tenuispinis Günther, 1862. China.
Platyglossus tremebundus Jordan & Snyder, 1902. Japan.

Subtropical Japan to Hong Kong region, slight differences in colour between Japan and Hong Kong populations. Occurs in small groups on kelp reefs, usually with a colourful dominating male in charge. Juveniles with a distinct ocellus in the dorsal fin and a black spot on the caudal fin base. Females sometimes have a black spot in either position, sometimes they have none. A small species, length to 12 cm.

A
H. tenuispinis. Male display. Osezaki, Japan. Depth 8 m. Length 12 cm.

B
H. tenuispinis. Male display. Ehime, Japan. D. 3 m. L. 12 cm. T. Hirata.

D

E

C
H. tenuispinis. Male. Izu, Japan. Depth 6 m. Length 11 cm.

F

H. tenuispinis. Juvenile stages. Japan. **D** Ehime. Length 10 mm. **E** Kochi. Length 11 mm. **F** Kochi. Length 15 mm. Depths 4–7 m. Tomonori Hirata.

G
H. tenuispinis. Izu, Japan. Depth 16 m. Length 10 cm.

H
H. tenuispinis. Izu, Japan. Depth 25 m. Length 8 cm.

I
H. tenuispinis. Kashiwajima, Japan. Depth 15 m. Length 9 cm.

J
H. tenuispinis. Kochi, Japan. D. 18 m. L. 40 mm. T. Hirata.

False-eyed Wrasse *Halichoeres biocellatus*

Halichoeres biocellatus Schultz, 1960. Bikini Atoll.

Widespread West Pacific, ranging to sub-tropical zones. Coastal to outer reef crests and slopes on rocky or rubble-algae substrates. Readily identified by body colour and distinct ocelli in dorsal fin in young and females. Length to 12 cm.

A

H. biocellatus. Male. Aquarium grown from Sydney. Length 12 cm.

B

H. biocellatus. Kochi, Japan. L. 20 mm. T. Hirata.

C

H. biocellatus. Male. Rowley Shoals, WA. Depth 10 m. Length 12 cm.

D

H. biocellatus. Juv. NSW, Australia. L. 25 mm.

E

H. biocellatus. Male. Bali, Indonesia. Depth 10 m. Length 12 cm.

F

H. biocellatus. Juv. NSW, Australia. L. 35 mm.

G

H. biocellatus. Female. Flores, Indonesia. Depth 6 m. Length 10 cm.

H

H. biocellatus. Juv. NSW, Australia. L. 45 mm.

I

H. biocellatus. Aberration. Kochi, Japan. D. 9 m. L. 50 mm. T. Hirata.

Ornate Wrasse *Halichoeres ornatissimus*

Julis ornatissimus Garrett, 1863. Hawaiian Is.

Uncertain distribution. Hawaiian region. Several similar species in West Pacific and Indian Ocean. Most juveniles and female stages of the species feature two ocelli in the dorsal fin, one in the centre and one at the end. The latter persists longest before fading altogether. Occurs commonly in the Hawaiian islands on shallow reefs. Length to 15 cm.

H. ornatissimus. Male. Hawaii, aquarium. Length 15 cm.

Red-scribbled Wrasse *Halichoeres* sp 2

undetermined species, appears to be undescribed.

West Pacific, Indonesia to Ogasawara I, Japan. Previously included with *Halichoeres ornatissimus*. In this species the ocellus in the centre of the dorsal fin persists until adult stage and even shows in most males, as is the case in *H. cosmetus*. Clear reef habitats, usually seen singly in 6–20 m depth. Length to 12 cm.

A

H. sp. Male. Flores, Indonesia. Depth 6 m. Length 12 cm.

B

H. sp. Flores, Indonesia. Depth 6 m. Length 55 mm.

C

H. sp. Flores, Indonesia. Depth 15 m. Length 45 mm.

Adorned Wrasse *Halichoeres cosmetus*

Halichoeres cosmetus Randall & Smith, 1982. Maldives.

Indian Ocean, a common species in the Maldives. Occurs on shallow rubble-reef patches on flats and slopes to about 20 m depth. Usually in small groups swimming close to the sea bed. Small juveniles secretive amongst large rubble pieces. Juveniles with very prominent ocelli in the dorsal fin that persist to adult stages but fade in large males, just appearing as a proportionally small red spot in the centre of the fin. Length to 12 cm.

A

H. cosmetus. Male. Maldives. Depth 18 m. Length 12 cm.

B

H. cosmetus. Female. Maldives. Depth 15 m. Length 10 cm.

C

H. cosmetus. Maldives. Depth 12 m. Length 35 mm.

Jewelled Wrasse *Halichoeres lapillus*

Halichoeres lapillus Smith, 1947. Delagoa.

Western Indian Ocean, Mozambique, Madagascar and Mauritius. Occurs on weed-dominated reefs to about 15 m depth. Identified by their generally green colour with pearly spots and the diagnostic dark bars on the lower half of the head. Length to 14 cm.

H. lapillus. Aquarium, origin unknown. L. 8 cm. Helmut Debelius.

Green-cheek Wrasse *Halichoeres orientalis*

Halichoeres orientalis Randall, 1999. Okinawa.

Southern Japan and Taiwan. Reported, in Japanese literature, as *Halichoeres ornatissimus*, a Hawaiian species. Occurs on shallow rocky and coral reefs to about 15 m depth. Distinctive colouration. Juveniles and young females have two large ocelli in the dorsal fin. Males are green with orange stripes and have a distinctive bright green cheek with a single horizontal orange-red stripe. Length to 15 cm.

A

H. orientalis. Male. Kochi Japan. D. 11 m. L. 15 cm. Tomonori Hirata.

B

C

D

H. orientalis. Kochi Japan. **B** Juvenile. D. 5 m. L. 2 cm. **C** Female. D. 15 m. L. 7 cm. **D** Male. D. 14 m. L. 13 cm. **B–D** Tomonori Hirata.

E

F

H. orientalis. Japan. **E** Female. Iriomote I. Depth 25 m. Length 11 cm. **F** Male. Kerama I. Depth 12 m. Length 14 cm.

A

H. margaritaceus. Male. Kochi, Japan. D. 3 m. L. 11 cm. Tomonori Hirata.

Pearly Wrasse *Halichoeres margaritaceus*

Julis margaritaceus Valenciennes, 1839. Vanicoro.

Widespread West Pacific. Coastal, shallow and usually algae-rocky reefs. Often in moderate surge zones. One of several similar species that have near identical juvenile and female stages. Males can be distinguished by their different cheek patterns, and this species has a near horizontal pink band below the eye. Juveniles are most similar to *Halichoeres nebulosus*, but are more slender. Length to 12 cm.

B

H. margaritaceus. Okinawa, Japan. D. 3 m. L. 11 cm. Tomonori Hirata.

C

NSW, Australia. Aquarium. Length 25 mm.

D

H. margaritaceus. Male. Sangihe I, Indonesia. Depth 2 m. Length 10 cm.

E

NSW, Australia. Aquarium. Length 35 mm.

F

G

H. margaritaceus. Females. **F** Guam. Depth 5 m. Length 11 cm. **G** NSW, Australia. Aquarium. Length 9 cm.

H

I

H. margaritaceus. Females. NSW, Australia. **H** Depth 3 m. Length 11 cm. **I** Depth 6 m. Length 10 cm.

Clouded Wrasse *Halichoeres nebulosus*

Julis nebulosus Valenciennes, 1839. India.

Widespread Indo West Pacific, ranging to subtropical zones as adults. Mainly occurs on algae-rocky reefs in coastal waters. Shallow to at least 40 m depth. Males are identified by the angled or diagonal pink band below the eye. Females have a brighter pink patch of colour on the belly and are slightly deeper bodied compared to the similar *H. margaritaceus*. Length to 12 cm.

H. nebulosus. Male. NSW, Australia. Depth 4 m. Length 12 cm.

H. nebulosus. Kochi, Japan. Depth 4 m. **B** Juvenile. Length 25 mm. **C** Male. Length 10 cm. Tomonori Hirata.

H. nebulosus. **D** Female. Maldives. Depth 15 m. Length 65 mm. **E** Male. Bali, Indonesia. Depth 6 m. Length 12 cm.

H. nebulosus. Monte Bello I., WA. **F** Female. Depth 3 m. Length 75 mm. **G** Male. Depth 6 m. Length 11 cm.

H. nebulosus. Females. **H** Kochi, Japan. Depth 3 m. Length 4 cm. Tomonori Hirata. **I** NSW, Australia. Depth 6 m. Length 9 cm.

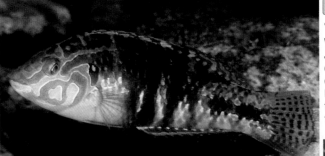

Cheek-ring Wrasse *Halichoeres miniatus*
Julis miniatus Valenciennes, 1839. Java.

Widespread West Pacific, but slightly different form in Japan. Coastal, in very shallow and usually algae-rocky coastal reefs. Males are distinguished by their ringed cheek pattern. Females have pink bellies with fine white lines along vertical scale-rows and finely speckled anal fins, usually with black spots, but red in Japanese form. Length to 12 cm.

H. miniatus. Bali, Indonesia. Depth 1 m. Length 12 cm.

H. miniatus. Ehime, Japan. D. 1 m. L. 40 mm. T. Hirata.

H. miniatus. Flores, Indonesia. **B** Depth 2 m. Length 10 cm. **D** Depth 1 m. Length 45 mm.

H. miniatus. Yeppoon, Qld, Australis. Depth 3 m. **E** Male. Length 10 cm. **F** Female. Length 60 mm.

H. miniatus. Aquarium, from Yeppoon, Qld, Australis. **G** Male. Length 11 cm. **H** Female. Length 10 cm.

130

Orange-fin Wrasse *Halichoeres melanochir*

Halichoeres melanochir Fowler & Bean, 1928.
Philippines.

West Pacific from southern Japan and Indonesia mainly west of Wallace's Line from northern Sulawesi to Bali, and a separate and distinctive variation in the North-west Cape region of western Australia. Coastal rocky reefs to about 25 m depth. Juvenile similar to small *H. annularis* and is distinguished from it by its orange ventral fin, which remains throughout its life. Length to 16 cm.

A

H. melanochir. Nuptial male. Sulawesi, Indonesia. D. 15 m. L. 15 cm.

B

C

H. melanochir. Bali, Indonesia. **B** Male. Depth 6 m. Length 14 cm. **C** Juvenile. Depth 15 m. Length 35 mm.

D

F

H. melanochir. Female. Tulamben, Bali. Depth 6 m. Length 12 cm.

G

E

H

H. melanochir. Japan. **E** Kerama. D. 20 m. L. 15 cm. **F-H** Kochi. Juveniles, **F** 35 mm. **G** 40 mm. **H** 50 mm. **F-H** Tomonori Hirata.

I

J

K

H. melanochir. Variation. Monte Bello I., WA. **I** Female. Depth 6 m. L. 12 cm. **J** Depth 8 m. L. 35 mm. **K** Depth 12 m. L. 25 mm.

131

Red Sea Dusky-wrasse *Halichoeres marginatus*

Halichoeres marginatus Rüppell, 1835. Red Sea.

Restricted to the Red Sea and Arabian Seas. Siblings in the Indo-West Pacific. Occurs on sheltered coastal reefs, often in silty habitats with rocks and urchins. Small juveniles secretive and often near urchins in narrow crevices. Small juveniles almost black with narrow white lines and spots, featuring two ocelli on the dorsal fin, centrally and posteriorly and one small one posteriorly on the anal fin. Males dusky to greenish with yellow-orange and blue-striped head. Length to 15 cm.

H. marginatus. Oman. Depth 12 m. **A** Male. Length 14 cm. **B** Female. Length 11 cm. **A** Juvenile. Length 75 mm. **A–C** Phil Woodhead.

Dusky-wrasse *Halichoeres lamarii*

Julis lamarii Valenciennes, 1839. Mauritius.

Widespread Indo-West Pacific, but two sub-species: *lamarii* in the western Indian Ocean and *annularis* elsewhere in the Indo-West Pacific, and latter has several geographical variations. *Halichoeres lamarii lamarii* has finer and much more numerous spotting in the median fins, especially on the caudal fin. Coastal to outer reefs on rock and rubble with mixed algae and invertebrate growth at various depths. Juveniles secretive in crevices, often with urchins. A drab species, although male can show metallic green and blue during display. Sub-tropical Japanese form has clear tail in initial stage and large males have vertical lines instead of small spots in the caudal fin. Length to 16 cm.

H. lamarii (subspecies *annularis*). Males. Bali, Indonesia. Depth 12 m. **A** Nuptial colours. Length 15 cm. **B** Non-excited colours.

H. annularis. Flores, Indonesia. Depth. 20 m. Lengths **C** 55 mm, **D** 9 cm.

H. lamarii (subspecies *lamarii*). **E** Female, Seychelles. **F** Male. Madagascar. Jerry Allen.

H. lamarii. Male. Maldives. Depth 15 m. Length 13 cm.

H. lamarii. Rowley Shoals, WA. **H** Female. Depth 6 m. Length 10 cm. **J** Male. Depth 5 m. Length 12 cm.

H. lamarii. Variation 1. Sydney, Australia. **I** Depth 4 m. L. 45 mm. **K** Female, aquarium. L. 85 mm.

H. lamarii. Male. Variation 2. Kerama. Depth 12 m. Length 15 cm.

H. lamarii. Variation 2. Ehime, Japan. **M** Depth 0.5 m. Length 35 mm. **N** Depth 5 m. Length 12 cm. Tomonori Hirata.

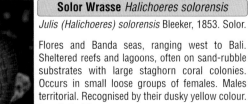

Solor Wrasse *Halichoeres solorensis*

Julis (Halichoeres) solorensis Bleeker, 1853. Solor.

Flores and Banda seas, ranging west to Bali. Sheltered reefs and lagoons, often on sand-rubble substrates with large staghorn coral colonies. Occurs in small loose groups of females. Males territorial. Recognised by their dusky yellow colour. Length to 14 cm.

H. solorensis. Male. Tulamben, Bali. Depth 10 m. Length 14 cm.

H. solorensis. Maumere, Flores. **B** Young male. Depth 15 m. Length 12 cm. **C** & **D** Depth 12 m. Length 45 mm.

H. solorensis. Maumere, Flores. Females. Depth 12-15 m. Length 10 cm.

Dark-side Wrasse *Halichoeres iridis*

Halichoeres iridis Randall & Smith, 1982. Mauritius.

Western Indian Ocean, ranging into the Red Sea but not known from the Maldives. Usually found at moderate depths over 20 m, but occasionally found in the shallows. Adults are readily identified by their unusual combination of colours, being dark but with an almost white back, but is obviously closely related to *Halichoeres chrysus*. Small juveniles have prominent ocelli in the dorsal fin that show as spots in females. Length to 11 cm.

H. iridis. Male. Kenya. Depth 25 m. Length 11 cm. Jerry Allen.

H. iridis. Oman. Depth 24 m. Length 10 cm. Phil Woodhead.

H. iridis. Kenya. Depth 25 m. Length 35 mm. Jerry Allen.

Yellow Wrasse *Halichoeres chrysus*

Halichoeres chrysus Randall, 1980.
Solomon Islands.

Widespread West Pacific, ranging to sub-tropical zones extending from Bali to Christmas Island in the Indian Ocean. Coastal to outer reef slopes, usually in small aggregations at all stages, in depths over 10 m. Readily identified by their bright yellow colour. Length to 10 cm.

H. chrysus. Male. Bali, Indonesia. Depth 15 m. Length 10 cm.

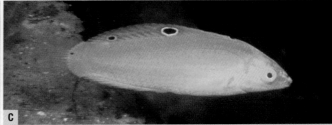

H. chrysus. NSW, Australia. **B** Sydney. Depth 18 m. Length 15 mm. **C** Montague I. Depth. 20 m. Length 65 mm.

H. chrysus. Kochi, Japan. **D** Depth 23 m. Length 15 mm. **E** Male. Depth. 24 m. Length. 10 cm. **D** & **E** Tomonori Hirata.

Lemon Meringue Wrasse
Halichoeres leucoxanthus

Halichoeres leucoxanthus
Randall & Smith, 1982. Java.

West Indian Ocean to Java. Along reef margins onto sand, usually about 15-30 m deep. In small groups. Easily identified by their mostly bright yellow body with white below. Length to 12 cm.

H. leucoxanthus. Maldives. Depth 15 m. **A** Courting male. Length 11 mm. **B** Juvenile. Length. 45 mm. **C** Female. Length. 10 cm.

Platyglossus xanti Karoli, 1882. Singapore.
Halichoeres melasmapomus Randall, 1980. Pitcairn I.

Widespread West Pacific, some variations. Coastal bays to outer reefs along drop-offs with caves and rich invertebrate habitats. Distinctive species with large bluish-black blotch behind eye. Juveniles and females with black spots at each end and one in centre of dorsal fin and an additional ocellus on the caudal fin base. Pink on outer reefs and more reddish inshore with longitudinal stripes along lower part of body. Adults occur in small groups. Juveniles solitary. Length to 12 cm.

H. xanti. Male. Flores, Indonesia. Depth 25 m. Length 12 cm.

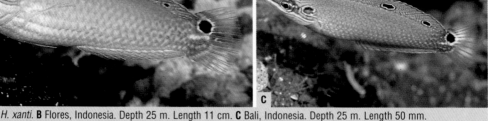

H. xanti. **B** Flores, Indonesia. Depth 25 m. Length 11 cm. **C** Bali, Indonesia. Depth 25 m. Length 50 mm.

H. xanti. Male. Tomini Bay, Sulawesi, Indonesia. Depth 10 m. Length 11 cm.   *H. xanti.* Male. Guam. Depth 30 m. Length 10 cm.

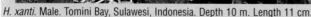

H. xanti. Variation. Rowley Shoals, WA. Depth 30 m. **F** Male. Length 11 cm. **G** Length 10 cm.

White Wrasse *Halichoeres trispilus*

Halichoeres trispilus Randall & Smith, 1982. Maldives.

Widespread Indian Ocean, ranging east to Java's south coast. Outer reef habitats, usually along deep drop-offs with large caves, rich with invertebrate growth in depths over 20 m. Occurs in small groups of females, usually with a male swimming nearby. Easily recognised at depth, as it appears to be almost white with some black spots or lines on the head. Length to 12 cm.

A

H. trispilus. Male. Pulabuhan Ratu, Java. Depth 30 m. Length 12 cm.

B

C

H. trispilus. Maldives. **B** Female. Depth 25 m. Length 8 cm. **C** Male. Depth 30 m. Length 10 cm.

Babi Wrasse *Halichoeres pallidus*

Halichoeres pallidus Kuiter & Randall, 1995. Gunung Api, Indonesia.

Flores and Banda Seas to Micronesia. Outer reef walls with large caves and rich invertebrate growth. Usually at depths of 30 m or more. Looks white at depth. Juveniles and females have three large black spots in dorsal fin. Occurs in small groups of females and a dominating male. Length to 10 cm.

A

H. pallidus. Male. Babi Island, Flores, Indonesia. Depth 30 m. Length 9 cm.

B

C

H. pallidus. Babi Island, Flores, Indonesia. Depth 30 m. **B** Juveniles. Lengths 3 cm. **C** Female. Length 8 cm.

Half-grey Wrasse *Halichoeres prosopeion*

Julis (Halichoeres) prosopeion Bleeker, 1853. Ambon.

Widespread West Pacific, ranging to sub-tropical zones, but Australian and eastern New Guinea form differs in colour. Coastal reef slopes and along drop-offs on the bottom of large caves. Usually seen singly. Australian juveniles white with black lines that continue to caudal fin. Indonesian form with yellow tail and stripes that fall well short of caudal fin. Adults with grey or blue-grey head with colour fading into light yellow about halfway along. Length to 12 cm.

H. prosopeion. Male. Bali, Indonesia. Depth 15 m. Length 12 cm.

H. prosopeion. Juveniles, length 40–45 mm. **B** Bali, Indonesia. **C** Kochi, Japan. Tomonori Hirata. **D** GBR, Australia (Australian form).

H. prosopeion. Changing colours. **E** Bali, Indonesia. D. 10 m. L. 75 mm. **F** Kochi, Japan. D. 18 m. L. 50 mm. **F** Tomonori Hirata.

H. prosopeion. Variation. NSW, Australia. Grown in aquarium. **G** Length 10 cm. **H** Length 50 mm.

H. prosopeion. Variation. **I** Papua New Guinea. D. 25 m. L. 12 cm. **J** GBR, Australia. D. 20 m. L. 12 cm.

138

Checkerboard Wrasse
Halichoeres hortulanus

Labrus hortulanus Lacepède, 1801.Mauritius.

Widespread Indo-West Pacific. Slight geographical variations between Indian and Pacific Oceans, and Red Sea. Various reef habitats, from coastal shallow reef crests and slopes to moderate depths along drop-offs. Adults with one or two yellow saddles over the back and sometimes with a small black spot on upper peduncle. Small juveniles black and white, gradually changing with growth to adult's pattern. Length to 25 cm.

A. *H. hortulanus*. Male. Red Sea. Depth 20 m. Length 22 cm.

B. *H. hortulanus*. Red Sea. L. 25 mm.

C. *H. hortulanus*. Male. Maldives. Depth 20 m. Length 22 cm.

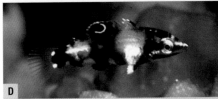

D. *H. hortulanus*. Bali, Indonesia. L. 20 mm.

F. *H. hortulanus*. NSW, Australia. L. 10 mm.

H. *H. hortulanus*. NSW, Australia. L. 25 mm.

G. *H. hortulanus*. Male. Flores, Indonesia. Depth 20 m. Length 22 cm.

H. hortulanus. Rowley Shoals, WA. **I** Depth 6 m. Length 10 cm. **J** Male. Depth 10 m. Length 23 cm.

E. *H. hortulanus*. Male. Bali. Indonesia. Depth 8 m. Length 24 cm.

Green-tail Wrasse *Halichoeres podostigma*

Julis (Halichoeres) podostigma Bleeker, 1854. Flores, Indonesia.

Known from Flores to Bali, Banda Seas and eastern Kalimantan. Clear coastal to outer reef crests with rich coral and hydrozoan growth. Usually seen singly. Juveniles easily recognised by their green tail, and adults by their generally unusual colouration. Length to 18 cm.

H. podostigma. Female. Maumere, Flores. Depth 10 m. Length 15 cm.

H. podostigma. Bali, Indonesia. **B** Male. Depth 12 m. Length 18 cm. **D** Length 45 mm. **C** Kalimantan, Indonesia. Depth 10 m. Length 25 mm.

Dark-blotch Wrasse
Halichoeres chloropterus

Labrus chloropterus Bloch, 1791. Japan (probably from Philippines).

Widespread West Pacific. Shallow inshore algae rubble reefs and lagoons. Juveniles bright green in algae habitat, but pale or with longitudinal dark bands on plain rubble. Usually with fine black spotting and a dark blotch as shown in **A**. Length to 18 cm.

H. chloropterus. Female. Maumere, Flores. Depth 6 m. Length 15 cm.

H. chloropterus. Java, Indonesia. **B** Male. D. 3 m. L. 18 cm. **C** D. 4 m. L. 25 mm. **D** Togean, Indonesia. D. 4 m. L. 50 mm. Jerry Allen.

Masculine. Type species: *Julis geoffroyi* Quoy & Gaimard, ,1824. A small Indo-Pacific genus with 10 species, variously distributed. Some have a small geographical range.

1 *Macropharyngodon bipartitus* Smith, 1957 **Splendid Leopard-wrasse** (p. 144)
2 *Macropharyngodon choati* Randall, 1978 **Choat's Leopard-wrasse** (p. 145)
3 *Macropharyngodon cyanoguttatus* Randall, 1978 **Blue-spotted Leopard-wrasse** (p. 145)
4 *Macropharyngodon geoffroyi* (Quoy & Gaimard, 1824) **Short-nose Leopard-wrasse** (N.A.)
5 *Macropharyngodon kuiteri* Randall, 1978 **Kuiter's Leopard-wrasse** (p. 146)
6 *Macropharyngodon meleagris* (Valenciennes, 1839) **Leopard Wrasse** (p. 142)
7 *Macropharyngodon moyeri* Shepard & Meyer, 1978 **Moyer's Leopard-wrasse** (p. 146)
8 *Macropharyngodon negrosensis* Herre, 1932 **Black Leopard-wrasse** (p. 147)
9 *Macropharyngodon ornatus* Randall, 1978 **Ornate Leopard-wrasse** (p. 143)
10 *Macropharyngodon vivienae* Randall, 1978 **Vivien's Leopard-wrasse** (p. 147)

Macropharyngodon bipartitus. Male, length about 13 cm. Maldives.

These small and usually very colourful fishes are known as leopard-wrasses due to their spotted pattern. Because of their small size and attractive colouration, they are sought after for the aquarium. They are easily kept, as long as conditions that suit them are provided. Leopard wrasses normally occur on sand and rubble type sea beds, usually with some algae growth, where they seek out small invertebrates as prey. It should be kept in mind that they like some open space and the bottom of a tank should have areas of fine sand with some small rocks scattered or piled near larger ones. It is important to provide fine sand when keeping juveniles so they can bury themselves safely. Best to start with some juveniles and let them develop. Usually one turns male. Introducing new individuals into a tank of established ones of the same genus can cause fights, especially when there is an established male.

Macropharyngodon kuiteri. Male, showing its teeth whilst yawning. The genus-name is in reference to the pair of enlarged canines in the upper jaw, near the corner of the mouth.

A

M. meleagris. Aquarium. NSW, Australia specimen. Length 13 cm.

Leopard Wrasse *Macropharyngodon meleagris*

Julis meleagris Valenciennes, 1839. Ulea.

West Pacific from Japan to Australia and northern Indonesia, ranging along Wallace's line to north-west Bali. Replaced by *M. ornatus* in most of Indonesia, but co-occurs with this species in the Rowley Shoals, WA. Shallow coastal to outer reef crests. Young and females light green with brown to black spots. Males reddish brown to green with iridescent dark-green spots on the body and lines on the head. A dark 'ear' spot with some yellow colouration. Length usually to 11 cm, but males can reach 14 cm in some subtropical regions.

B

M. meleagris. Male. Sangihe I. Indonesia. Depth 6 m. Length 10 cm.

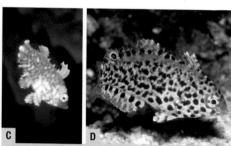

C

D

M. meleagris. Montague I. NSW. Lengths: 15–30 mm.

E

F

M. meleagris. **E** Female, Mabul, Malaysia. Depth 10 m. Length 8 cm. **F** Kerama, Japan. Depth 12 m. Length 75 mm.

G

H

I

M. meleagris. Rowley Shoals, WA. 15–25 m. **G** Male. Length 12 cm. **H** Juvenile 25 mm. **I** Female, 11 cm, together with *M. ornatus.*

Ornate Leopard-wrasse
Macropharyngodon ornatus

Macropharyngodon ornatus Randall, 1978. Ambon.

True species in the Moluccas to Flores sea. Variation 1 a separate population in southern-tropical Western Australia, and variation 2 widespread Indian Ocean, ranging east to Bali. Various reef habitats on rubble to about 30 m depth. Females usually in small groups, dominated by a territorial male. Length to 11 cm.

A
M. ornatus. Male. Flores, Indonesia. Depth 6 m. Length 11 cm.

B
M. ornatus. Flores, Indonesia. D. 6 m. L. 9 cm.

M. ornatus. Variation 1. Monte Bellow Islands, WA. Depth 15 m. **C** Female. Length 9 cm. **D** Male. Length 10 cm.

M. ornatus. Variation 2 (Indian Ocean). Java, Indonesia. **E** depth 15 m. L. 8 cm. **F** depth 5 m. L. 10 cm. **G** depth 15 m L. 10 cm.

143

Macropharyngodon bipartitus Smith, 1957.
Pinta, Mozambique.

Western Indian Ocean to the Maldives and Red
Sea. Occurs on invertebrate-rich reefs in clear
habitats to about 30 m depth. Juveniles and
females occur in small groups, usually with a
colourful male nearby. Also known as Divided
or Vermiculate Wrasse. Length to 13 cm.

M. bipartitus. Male. Maldives. Depth 18 m. Length 13 cm.

M. bipartitus. Males, nuptial colours. **B** Red Sea. Depth 23 m. Length 12 cm. **C** Maldives. Depth 18 m. Length 12 cm.

M. bipartitus. Maldives. Depth 8–15 m. **D** Changing sex to male. L. 10 cm. **E** Juveniles. L. 35 mm. **F** Females. L. 85 mm.

Blue-spotted Leopard-wrasse
Macropharyngodon cyanoguttatus

Macropharyngodon cyanoguttatus Randall, 1978. Mauritius.

Only known from the Western Indian Ocean, ranging from South Africa (Natal) to Réunion and Mauritius. Occurs on rubble reefs in 15–50 m depth range. Usually in small groups or pairs. Length to 12 cm.

A

B

M. cyanoguttatus. Kwazulu-Natal, South Africa. Depth about 20 m. **A** Young female. **B** Male. **A** & **B** Dennis King.

Choat's Leopard-wrasse
Macropharyngodon choati

Macropharyngodon choati Randall, 1978. One Tree I., Qld.

Only known from eastern Australia and New Caledonia. Occurs on sheltered inner reefs, usually where there is good algae growth or some *Sargassum*. Some 10 mm juveniles were found amongst sparse seagrass on muddy substrates at 4–5 m depth in Sydney. This beautiful species is easily identified by its unique colouration. Males have a pale blue cheek. Length to 10 cm.

A

M. choati. Male. Southern Qld, Australia. Depth 8 m. Length 10 cm.

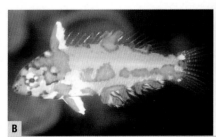

B

C

M. choati. Juveniles. NSW, Australia. **B** Sydney. Depth 15 m. Length 25 mm. **C** North Solitary I. Depth 23 m. Length 12 & 20 mm.

D

E

M. choati. Females. Queensland, Australia. **D** Lizard I., Depth 6 m. Length 8 cm. **E** Keppel I. Depth 8 m. Length 9 cm.

A

M. kuiteri. One Tree I., Qld. Depth 25 m. Length 10 cm.

Kuiter's Leopard-wrasse
Macropharyngodon kuiteri

Macropharyngodon kuiteri Randall, 1978.
NSW, Australia.

Eastern Australia from the capricorn region to northern NSW, but juveniles expatriate far south, and New Caledonia. Various reef habitats to about 30 m depth, adults usually at depths over 20 m. Juveniles on algae reefs near sand and rubble zones. Closely related to *Macropharyngodon moyeri* and *M. vivienae*. Identified by their distinctive colouration. Length to 10 cm.

B

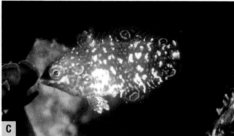

C

M. kuiteri. Sydney, NSW, Australia. **B** Aquarium grown male. Length 9 cm. **C** Depth 10 m. Length 20 mm.

D

E

M. kuiteri. NSW, Australia. **D** Seal Rocks. Aquarium grown female. Length 75 mm. **E** Montague I. Depth 12 m. Length 35 mm.

Moyer's Leopard-wrasse
Macropharyngodon moyeri

Macropharyngodon moyeri Shepard & Meyer, 1978.
Izu Islands, Japan.

Only known from the Izu Islands to the northern Ryukyu Islands. Occurs on algae sand and rubble reefs at a depth range of about 5 to 20 m. Closely related to *Macropharyngodon kuiteri* and males in particular are very similar in colouration. Length to 10 cm.

B

A

M. moyeri. Kochi, Japan. Depth 7 m. **A** Female. Length 8 cm. **B** Juvenile. Length 50 mm. **A** & **B** Tomonori Hirata.

Vivien's Leopard-wrasse
Macropharyngodon vivienae

Macropharyngodon vivienae Randall, 1978. Madagascar.

Known only from Madagascar and the eastern African coast from Natal south to Durban. Various reef habitats to about 40 m depth, adults usually at depths of over 20 m. Juveniles on algae reefs near sand and rubble zones. Juveniles and females have ocelli in the dorsal and anal fins. Length to 11 cm.

M. vivienae. Female. Kwazulu-Natal, South Africa. Dennis King.

Black Leopard-wrasse
Macropharyngodon negrosensis

Macropharyngodon negrosensis Herre, 1932. Philippines.

Widespread West Pacific, ranging to sub-tropical zones as larval stage is carried by currents. Deep coastal slopes, soft-bottom habitats or reef margins onto sand and rubble, usually deeper than 15 m. Young often in pairs or small loose groups, swimming close to the sea bed. When approached they move up and down in an unusual way that may worry a possible predator. Adults move about in small groups. Males display with a metallic green colour that is turned on for the occasion. Length to 10 cm.

M. negrosensis. Nuptial male. Flores, Indonesia. Depth 20 m. Length 10 cm.

M. negrosensis. Juveniles. **B** & **C** Kochi, Japan. D. 23 & 26 m. L. 12 & 15 mm. Tomonori Hirata. **D** Sydney, Austr. D. 9 m. L. 18 mm.

M. negrosensis. **E** Sydney, Australia. D. 10 m. L. 35 mm. **F** Bali, Indonesia. Female left, male right. Depth 20 m.

M. negrosensis. Sydney, Austr. D. 12. L. 45 mm.   *M. negrosensis.* Kochi, Japan. D. 20 m. L 10 cm. T. Hirata.

Genus *Xenojulis* de Beaufort, 1939

Feminine. Type species: *Xenojulis montillai* de Beaufort, by original designation (= ? *X. margaritacea*). An apparently monotypic genus from the Western Pacific, but living colours are not known for all populations and the Philippines populations may represent a second valid species. The only recognised species resembles some members of *Halichoeres,* but appears to be more closely related to *Macropharyngodon,* but certain features may have developed because of its adaptation to weed beds.

Pearly weed-wrasse
Xenojulis margaritacea

Platyglossus margaritaceus Macleay, 1884
Port Moresby, Papua New Guinea.

Known from across northern Australia and southern New Guinea. Possibly another population in the Philippines, but this appears to be different in colouration and *Xenojulis montillai* is its valid name. The Philippine males have a small pearly spot on most scales below the lateral line, forming a series of dotted lines. *X. margaritacea* has a broad, red-edged irregular pearly stripe from the axil towards the tail-base, that may vary in large individuals to large pearly blotches. Females have several ocelli in the dorsal and anal fins and these are very prominent features in juveniles (not seen). These fishes are exclusively found on rubble with dense algae growth, usually at just a few metres depth. They occur in loose aggregations of females and a dominating male. Length to 10 cm in WA and 12 cm in the Philippines.

X. margaritacea. Monte Bellow Islands, Western Australia. Depth 2–3 m. **A & B** Male. Length 9 cm. **C** Female. Length 85 mm.

GENUS *Ophthalmolepis* Bleeker, 1862

Feminine. Type species: *Julis lineolatus* Valenciennes, 1838. A monotypic genus from sub-temperate to sub-tropical Australian waters. Very similar to the genus *Coris* in shape and behaviour. The colouration is also like some of the species of *Coris*. It has a blunter head and fewer scales than most species of that genus. *Ophthalmolepis* has 52–56 scales along the lateral line, whilst most *Coris* range between 70–90, except *C. pictoides* with only 48–50.

Australian Maori-wrasse
Ophthalmolepis lineata

Julis lineolatus Valenciennes, 1838.
Victoria, Australia.

Southern half of Australia, except Tasmania. Rocky reefs with algae or sponges. Adults occur mainly on deeper offshore reefs to a depth of at least 60 m, where often aggregate in large numbers. Small juveniles solitary in estuaries and harbours amongst rocks. Identified by their distinctive colouration at all stages. Length to 40 cm.

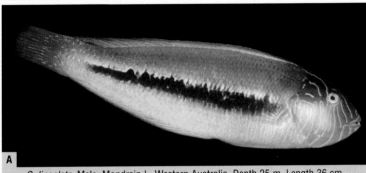

A · *O. lineolata*. Male. Mondrain I., Western Australia. Depth 25 m. Length 36 cm.

B

C

D

O. lineata. Juvenile stages.
Sydney, Australia. Depths: 5–10 m.
Lengths: **B** 23 mm. **C** 62 mm. **B** 85 mm.

E · *O. lineolata*. Female. Southern NSW, Australia. Depth 20 m. Length 24 cm.

F · *O. lineolata*. Female. Southern NSW, Australia. Depth 25 m. Length 15 cm.

G · *O. lineolata*. Male. Southern NSW, Australia. Depth 25 m. Length 40 cm.

Feminine. Type species: *Coris aygula* Lacepède, 1801. A tropical wrasse genus with 27 species, 2 of which are in the Atlantic Ocean and Mediterranean and with the remainder variously distributed throughout the Indo-Pacific and Red Sea.

1 *Coris atlantica* Günther, 1862 **Atlantic Rainbow-wrasse** (p. 163)
2 *Coris auricularis* (Valenciennes, 1839) **Western King-wrasse** (p. 155)
3 *Coris aurilineata* Randall & Kuiter, 1982 **Yellow-lined Rainbow-wrasse** (p. 166)
4 *Coris aygula* Lacepède, 1801 **Clown Rainbow-wrasse** (p. 152)
5 *Coris ballieui* Vaillant & Sauvage, 1875 **Lined Rainbow-wrasse** (N.A.)
6 *Coris batuensis* (Bleeker, 1856) **Batu Rainbow-wrasse** (p. 164)
7 *Coris bulbifrons* Randall & Kuiter, 1982 **Double Header** (p. 159)
8 *Coris caudimacula* (Quoy & Gaimard, 1834) **Tail-spot Rainbow-wrasse** (p. 160)
9 *Coris centralis* Randall, 1999 **Central Pacific Wrasse** (N.A.)
10 *Coris cuvieri* Bennett, 1831 **African Rainbow-wrasse** (p. 157)
11 *Coris debuen* Randall, 1999 **Eastern Island Rainbow-wrasse** (N.A.)
12 *Coris dorsomacula* Fowler, 1908 **Pink-lined Rainbow-wrasse** (p. 161)
13 *Coris flavovittata* Bennett, 1829 **Hawaiian Rainbow-wrasse** (p. 153)
14 *Coris formosa* (Bennett, 1830) **Queen Rainbow-wrasse** (p. 158)
15 *Coris gaimard* (Quoy & Gaimard, 1824) **Gaimard Rainbow-wrasse** (p. 156)
16 *Coris hewetti* Randall, 1999 **Hewett's Rainbow-wrasse** (N.A.)
17 *Coris julis* (Linnaeus, 1758) **Europe's Rainbow-wrasse** (p. 162)
18 *Coris marquesensis* Randall, 1999 **Marquesas Rainbow-wrasse** (N.A.)
19 *Coris musume* Jordan & Snyder, 1902 **Japanese Comb-wrasse** (p. 169)
20 *Coris nigrotaenia* Mee & Hare, 1995 **Black-bar Rainbow-wrasse** (p. 163)
21 *Coris picta* (Bloch & Schneider, 1801) **Australian Comb-wrasse** (p. 168)
22 *Coris pictoides* Randall & Kuiter, 1982 **Pixy Rainbow-wrasse** (p. 167)
23 *Coris roseoviridis* Randall, 1999 **Rapa's Rainbow-wrasse** (N.A.)
24 *Coris sandageri* (Hector, 1884) **Eastern King-wrasse** (p. 154)
25 *Coris schroederii* (Bleeker, 1858) **Schroeder's Rainbow-wrasse** (p. 164)
26 *Coris variegata* (Rüppell, 1835) **Variegated Rainbow-wrasse** (p. 164)
27 *Coris venusta* Vaillant & Sauvage, 1875 **Elegant Rainbow-wrasse** (N.A.)

Coris bulbifrons. Lord Howe Island, NSW. Australia. The largest in the genus, males developing a large hump. Gary Bell.

Members of the genus *Coris* are commonly known as 'Rainbow-wrasses'. They feature numerous tiny scales and many are boldly coloured, especially when juveniles. Usually the various species are readily identified by their distinctive colour patterns. Many show dramatic changes during growth to such an extent that juveniles look nothing like their parents. It is a diverse genus, as presently classified, with a range size of just over 10 cm for the smallest, to about 1 m for the largest member. Some are localised in their geographical distribution, whilst others are widespread and show little variation over their large range. Most occur in tropical waters, but a few species are found in subtropical to subtemperate zones. They are typically found along reef edges that border onto sand and rubble, many species forming small aggregations of females with a territorial male taking charge of large sections of reef.

The brightly coloured juveniles of some species, especially *Coris gaimard* and *C. aygula*, are well known in the aquarium fish trade. They are very attractive looking fish that do well in captivity, but unfortunately these, and many other species, grow rather large. They change colour completely and need a lot of space as adults. All *Coris* spp bury themselves in sand to sleep at night, or to escape potential danger. To successfully raise small juveniles, it is important to have a patch of fine sand available in the aquarium. In the wild, many of these fish specially prepare several such places, just comprising of fine sand,carefully removing the larger grains. Some species have these patches distributed throughout their territory in such a way that they can roam large areas but always have somewhere close to escape to if there is a possible threat.

They feed on a wide variety of small invertebrates and will accept any type of meaty food. Several species were collected as tiny juveniles in Sydney waters and raised to adult with ease. Some species look for food underneath things and will turn over surprisingly large pieces of coral or rock. It is always a good thing to have some pieces of coral and rock in the aquarium to keep them entertained, especially when it is possible to supply live foods. Although none of the species are specialised cleaners like those in the genus *Labroides,* many species of *Coris* clean part-time as juveniles and, on a fairly regular basis, as adults, taking parasites from other fishes as part of their diet.

I found that rainbow wrasses are not aggressive towards other species and do well in community aquariums. They can certainly look after themselves, however, well established species may show aggression towards new members introduced into an aquarium, especially males. Introduction of new members to a marine aquarium is always tricky and rejection is most fierce towards their own or closely related species.

C. picta. Montague Island, NSW, Australia. Depth 25 m. Large juveniles and females, cleaning *Chromis hypsilepis.*

A

C. aygula. Rowley Shoals, Western Australia. Depth 10 m. Length 45 cm.

Clown Wrasse *Coris aygula*

Coris aygula Lacepède, 1801. Mauritius.

Widespread Indo-West Pacific, but appears to be absent in Flores and Banda seas. Ranges to sub-tropical zones as juveniles. Some geographical variations, especially between the Red Sea and the rest of the Indo-Pacific. Occurs on sheltered algae-rock reefs or sparse coral habitats, often in semi-exposed surge zones on shallow reef flats with gutters, where juveniles utilise the rubble on the sea bed. Juveniles distinctly coloured, pale, almost white, with false eyes on the dorsal fin, shaded by orange on the body below. Length to 60 cm.

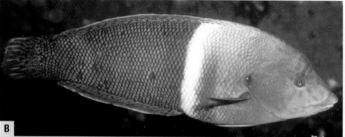

B

C

C. aygula. NSW, Australia. **B** Solitary Is. Depth 10 m. Length 40 cm. **C** Sydney. D. 10 m. L. 30 mm.

D

E

C. aygula. Iriomote, Japan. Depth 10 m. Length 10 cm.

F

C. aygula. Solitary Is. Depth 10 m. Length 14 cm.

C. aygula. Rowley Shoals, WA. D. 10 m. L. 10 cm.

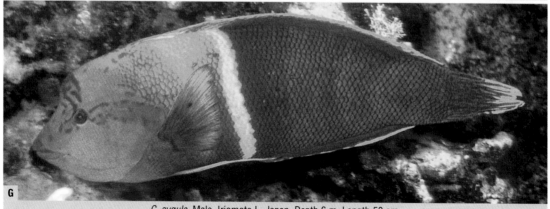

G

C. aygula. Male. Iriomote I., Japan. Depth 6 m. Length 50 cm.

C. aygula. Variation. Egypt, Red Sea. Depth 3–15 m. Lengths: **H** 25 mm. **I** 10 cm. **J** 16 cm. **K** 24 cm. **L** 35 cm. **M** 50 cm.

Hawaiian Rainbow-wrasse *Coris flavovittata*

Coris flavovittata Bennett, 1828. Hawaiian Islands.

Restricted to the Hawaiian Island region. Occurs on sand and rubble substrates adjacent to reefs. Juveniles black with thin white lines, changing to white with black lines as they grow into the female stage. Males change completely to a mottled pattern with green, pale blue and yellow with a dark caudal fin. Length to 18 cm.

C. flavovittata. Midway, Hawaiian Islands. **A** Initial phase, female. **B** Terminal phase, male. Length about 18 cm. Kendall Clements.

A

C. sandageri. Napier Aquarium, New Zealand. Length 40 cm.

Eastern King Wrasse *Coris sandageri*

Cymolutes sandeyeri Hector, 1884. New Zealand.

New Zealand to Norfolk Island region and subtropical eastern Australia. Occurs on coastal to offshore reefs near weed-covered rocks and sand. Females in small aggregations. Males patrol large reef sections, usually in depths between 20–40 m. Juveniles in more shallow waters. Changes from a lined to a barred pattern but is readily identified by the various colour patterns at different stages. Length to 45 cm.

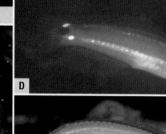

D

B

C. sandageri. Female. Sydney, NSW, Australia. D. 5 m. L. 25 cm.

E

F

C

C. sandageri. Female. Southern NSW, Australia. D. 25 m. L. 32 cm.

C. sandageri. Juveniles. NSW, Australia. **D & E** Montague I. D. 20 m. **E** Sydney. Depth 7 m. Lengths: **D** 25 mm. **E** 45 mm. **F** 60 mm.

G

C. sandageri. Male. Montague I., NSW, Australia. Depth. 20 m. L. 42 cm.

154

Western King Wrasse *Coris auricularis*

Julis auricularis Valenciennes, 1839. King Georges Sound, Western Australia.

South-western Australia. Occurs on clear coastal to offshore weed and sponge reefs near sand to about 45 m depth. Changes from broad-striped when juvenile to fine-lined when female. Males have a dark band centrally on the body with a white patch in front on the abdomen. Identified by the various colour patterns at different stages. Length to 32 cm.

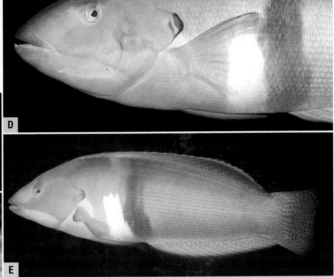

C. *auricularis*. Males. Canal Rocks, WA. Depth 15 m. Length 30 cm.

C. *auricularis*. **A** & **B** Juveniles. Cockburn Sound, WA. Depth 5 m. Length 50 mm. **C** Female. Eagle Bay, WA. Depth 4 m. Length 12 cm.

C. *auricularis*. Female. Canal Rocks, WA. Depth 15 m. Length 22 cm.

C. *auricularis*. Male. Nuptial colours. Canal Rocks, WA. Depth 15 m. Length 30 cm.

Julis gaimard Quoy & Gaimard, 1824.
Hawaiian Islands.

Widespread West Pacific. Similar species in Indian Ocean. Various reef habitats from shallow coastal rocky substrates to deep sand slopes. Juveniles easily recognised by their striking colouration. Females have a bright yellow caudal fin. Length to 30 cm.

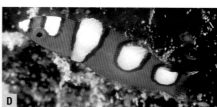

C. gaimard. Bali, Indonesia. Depth 6 m. **A** Male. L. 30 cm. **B** Female. L. 24 cm.

C. gaimard. Kerama, Japan. Depth 12 m. Length 12 cm.

C. gaimard. Juveniles. **D** Mabul, Malaysia. D. 10 m. L. 25 mm. **E** Sydney, Australia. Depth 7 m. L. 30 m. **F** Rowley Shoals, WA. D. 10 m. L. 10 cm.

C. gaimard. Nuptial male. Tulamben, Bali. Depth 6 m. Length 30 cm.

African Rainbow-wrasse *Coris cuvieri*

Julis cuvieri Bennett, 1831. Mauritius.

Widespread Indian Ocean, ranging east to Java. Closely related to *C. gaimard* (next species from Pacific waters and previously regarded as a sub-species. The two species overlap in range on Java's north coast. Coastal to outer reef habitats. Small juveniles on exposed reef flats with algae-rubble. Length to 35 cm.

D

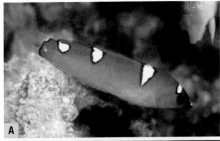

A

B

C

C. cuvieri. **A** Juvenile. Java. Depth 10 m. Length 7 cm. **B** & **C** Females. Maldives. Depth 24 m. Lengths: **B** 12 cm, **C** 24 cm.

E

C. cuvieri. Males. Maldives. Depth 12 m. Lengths 34 cm.

F

C. cuvieri. Egypt, Red Sea. Depth 20 m. Length 26 cm.

G

C. cuvieri. Female. Pulabuhan Ratu, Java. Depth 20 m. Length 20 cm.

H

C. cuvieri. Male. Nuptial colours. Maldives. Depth 12 m. Length 34 cm.

Queen Rainbow-wrasse *Coris formosa*

Labrus formosus Bennett, 1830. Sri Lanka.

Western Indian Ocean, ranging east to the Maldives and Sri Lanka. Occurs on rubble substrates on or near reefs. Adults usually at moderate depths, usually in 20 m or more, and juveniles on reef flats in rubble channels. Juveniles similar to *Coris cuvieri*, but have black ventral and anal fins and an eye-sized black spot in the dorsal fin. Adults have a distinctive colour pattern. Length to 50 cm.

C. formosa. Juveniles. **D** Maldives. Depth 6 m. Length 45 mm. **E** Maldives. Depth 7 m. Length 8 cm. Rob Myers. **F** Oman. Depth 15 m. Length 11 cm. Phil Woodhead.

C. formosa. Maldives. D. 25 m. **A** L. 14 cm. **B** L. 22 cm. **C** L. 35 cm.

C. formosa. Male. Maldives. Depth. 30 m. L. 45 cm.

Double Header *Coris bulbifrons*

Coris bulbifrons Randall & Kuiter, 1982.
Lord Howe Island, NSW. Australia.

Lord How and Norfolk Islands, stragglers to NSW coast. Sheltered reefs and lagoons. Juveniles distinguised by their colour and adults by their unusual head shape. The largest member of the genus *Coris*, reaching at least 1 m. Reported to 1.4 m.

A

B

C

C. bulbifrons. Sydney juveniles, collected from 5–8 m. In aquarium.
Lengths: **A** 25 mm, **B** 35 mm, **C** 65 mm.

D

C. bulbifrons. Male. Lord Howe Island, NSW. Australia. D. 10 m. L. 1 m. Gary Bell.

E

C. bulbifrons. Sydney specimen, collected from 5 m. Aquarium grown. Length 20 cm.

F

C. bulbifrons. Male. Lord Howe Island, NSW. Australia. D. 10 m. L. 1 m. Gary Bell.

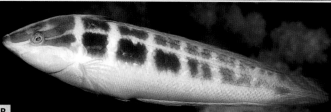

Tail-spot Rainbow-wrasse
Coris caudimacula

Julis caudimacula Quoy & Gaimard, 1834.
Mauritius.

Western Indian Ocean, Red Sea and Western Australia in several distinct populations. Geographical differences between the populations appear to be minor, but the Western Australian population has slightly different colour patterns at all stages. Occurs typically along reef margins bordering onto sand, usually at depths over 10 m. Juveniles and females are often seen in the same general area of the reef, the females in small loose groups with a male regularly visiting, usually giving a brief courtship display to each of the females, seemingly to remind them that he is around. This species is identified by its unique colour pattern. Length to 20 cm.

C. caudimacula. Egypt, Red Sea. Depth 10–20 m. **A–C** Males. Lengths 16–20 (**B** largest) cm. **D** Female. Length 14 cm.

C. caudimacula. Monte Bellow Islands, Western Australia. Depth 16 m. **E** Female. Length 12 cm. **F** Juvenile. Length 55 mm.

C. caudimacula. Nuptial male. Monte Bellow Islands, Western Australia. Depth 16 m. Length 16 cm.

Pink-lined Rainbow-wrasse
Coris dorsomacula

Coris dorsomacula Fowler, 1908.
Victoria (= Kimberleys), NW Australia.

Widespread West Pacific, ranging to sub-tropical zones as adults. Coastal to outer reef habitats in deep gutters or along reef margins, favouring rocky substrates with sand flats from 3 to 30 m. Juveniles often on algae-rubble. Body of adults greenish with pink longitudinal lines and white barring. Length to 20 cm.

A

C. dorsomacula. Male. Bali, Indonesia. Depth 10 m. Length 18 cm.

B

C

D

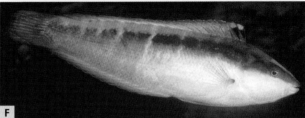

F

C. dorsomacula. Male. NSW, Australia. Depth 20 m. Length 18 cm.

E

G

C. dorsomacula. Male. Izu, Japan. Depth 10 m. Length 18 cm.

C. dorsomacula. NSW, Australia. **B-D** Sydney. Depths 5–10 m. Lengths 30–60 mm. **E** Montague Island. Depth 22 m. Length 10 cm.

H

C. dorsomacula. Female. NSW, Australia. Depth 24 m. Length 12 cm.

I

C. dorsomacula. Male. Sydney, NSW, Australia. Depth 10 m. Length 18 cm.

161

Labrus julis Linnaeus, 1758. Genoa, Italy.

Mediterranean, Black Sea and eastern Atlantic, ranging to Sweden in the north, Azores west and south to Port Gentil on the African continent. Occurs mainly on shallow algae reefs and seagrass habitats, sometimes forming large aggregations in which females greatly out-number males. Males are identified by their orange to red mid-lateral stripe with a black blotch above the abdomen. Length of males to 25 cm and females to 18 cm.

C. julis. Male. Costa Blanca. Depth 10 m. Length 18 cm. Helmut Debelius.

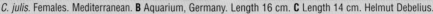

C. julis. Females. Mediterranean. **B** Aquarium, Germany. Length 16 cm. **C** Length 14 cm. Helmut Debelius.

C. julis. Male. Aquarium, Germany. Length 22 cm.

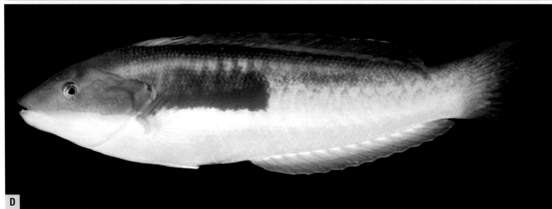

C. julis. Males and females mixed, plus some *Thalassoma pavo*. Mediterranean. Depth 10 m. Helmut Debelius.

Atlantic Rainbow-wrasse *Coris atlantica*

Coris atlantica Günther, 1862. Sierra Leone.

Eastern Atlantic, ranging from the Cape Verdi Islands to Portugal. Occurs on algae and sponge reefs to about 50 m depth and reported to 120 m. Previously confused with or considered a colour variation of the more common *Coris julis*. Males are identified by their comb-patterned mid-lateral stripe and juvenile and females have a black mid-lateral stripe. Length to 24 cm.

C. atlantica. Male. Portugal. Depth 15 m. Length 18 cm. Phil Woodhead.

C. atlantica. Portugal. Depth 10 m. Length: **B** 45 mm, **C** 16 cm, **D** 11 cm. Phil Woodhead.

Black-bar Rainbow-wrasse
Coris nigrotaenia

Coris nigrotaenia Mee & Hare, 1995. Oman.

Appears to be endemic to the southern region of Oman. Occurs on rocky reefs, often in high energy zones. Juveniles in algae habitats, generally weed coloured with large white blotches. Females have a dark bar above the abdomen that reduces to a blotch in large individuals, and males are similar to the large females, but does not have the central blotch and looks more blue. Length to 40 cm.

C. nigrotaenia. Female. Oman. Depth 15 m. Length 30 cm. Phil Woodhead.

163

Halichoeres variegatus Rüppell, 1835. Red Sea.

Endemic to the Red Sea. The name is often wrongly used for *Coris schroederii*, its Indo-Pacific sibling. Occurs on sand and rubble substrates adjacent to reefs, usually at depths of 15 m or more. A pale, sandy-coloured species with a few dusky and red speckles. Juveniles with two distinct ocelli in the dorsal fin that proportionally reduce in size with age. The centrally placed one may be present as a small dark spot. Males and females are very similar, unlike most other wrasses. Usually seen singly or in small loose aggregations swimming close to the substrate. Length to 14 cm.

C. variegata. Egypt, Red Sea. Depth 20 m. Length 12 cm. Helmut Debelius.

C. variegata. Red Sea. Depth 20 m. Length 14 cm. Jerry Allen.

Batu Rainbow-wrasse *Coris batuensis*

Julis (Halichoeres) batuensis Bleeker, 1856. Batu Islands, Indonesia.

Only known from the type specimen, but the area of the type-locality off the west Sumatra coast is relatively unexplored and it seems that it is restricted to that area. Several other wrasses *(Cirrhilabrus adornus, Halichoeres kallochroma)* are primarily known from there. It has the same meristic counts as *Coris schroederii*, but is more slender (height almost 5x total length versus 4x). The markings on the head and fins are distinctive and probably diagnostic. Length 15 cm.

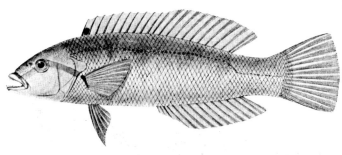

C. batuensis. Type from Batu. Length 15 cm. After Bleeker.

Schroeder's Rainbow-wrasse
Coris schroederii

Julis (Halichoeres) schroederii Bleeker, 1858. Ambon.

Widespread Indo-West Pacific, but some colour differences between Indian and Pacific Oceans. Replaced by *C. variegata* in the Red Sea. Coastal reef flats and slopes and in sandy lagoons. Greenish with pink markings on dark substrate. Very pale when on white sand substrates and dorsal spots are lost in large males. Length to 17 cm.

C. schroederii. Male. Bali, Indonesia Depth 10 m. Length 12 cm.

C. schroederii. Female. PNG Depth 16 m. Length 10 cm.

C. schroederii. Sydney, Australia. Depth 5 m. Length 45 mm.

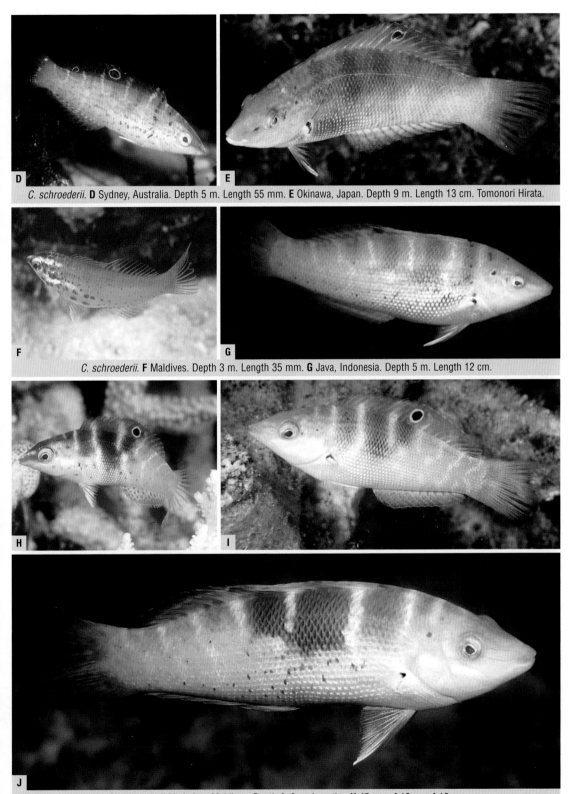

C. schroederii. **D** Sydney, Australia. Depth 5 m. Length 55 mm. **E** Okinawa, Japan. Depth 9 m. Length 13 cm. Tomonori Hirata.

C. schroederii. **F** Maldives. Depth 3 m. Length 35 mm. **G** Java, Indonesia. Depth 5 m. Length 12 cm.

C. schroederii. Variation. Maldives. Depth 6–9 m. Lengths: **H** 45 mm, **I** 12 cm, **J** 16 cm.

Yellow-lined Rainbow-wrasse
Coris aurilineata

Coris auriliniata Randall & Kuiter, 1982. Qld, Australia.

Only known from Australia's east coast from the Keppel I. Qld to Bass Point in NSW. Occurs on shallow rocky and algae reef habitats to about 10 m depth, entering harbours. Adults in small aggregations, usually roaming over large reef areas. Juveniles solitary and more secretive amongst weeds. Colouration is much like some *Halichoeres* spp, but readily distinguished from them by the much more numerous, smaller scales on the body. Length to 14 cm.

C. aurilineata. Keppel I., Qld, Australia. Depth 5 m. **A** Male, length 14 cm. **B** Female, length 12 cm. **C** Juvenile, length 55 mm.

C. aurilineata. NSW, Australia. **D** Bass Point. D. 10 m. L. 75 mm. **E** Sydney. D. 6 m. L. 50 mm. **F** Seal Rocks. D. 4 m. L. 10 cm.

C. aurilineata. Male. Sydney Harbour, Australia. Depth 6 m. Length 12 cm.

Pixy Rainbow-wrasse
Coris pictoides

Coris pictoides Randall & Kuiter, 1982. Tioman Island, Malaysia.

Widespread West Pacific, ranging to sub-tropical zones, but eastern Australian population differs considerably in colour. Coastal to outer reef slopes and deep lagoons. Occurs in small groups on sandy or muddy substrates along reef margins or on soft sea beds. Enters shallow estuaries as well. Readily identified by their colour and small scales. Length usually to 11 cm.

A

C. pictoides. Male. Flores, Indonesia. Depth 20 m. Length 10 cm.

B

D

C. pictoides. Male. Bali, Indonesia. Depth 6 m. Length 11 cm.

C

C. pictoides. Monte Bellos, WA. **B** Juvenile. Depth 9 m. Length 20 mm. **C** Female. Depth 12 m. Length 75 mm.

E

C. pictoides. Sydney juvenile, aquarium grown. Length 45 mm.

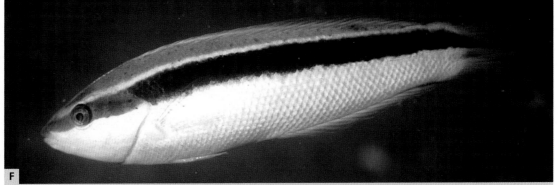

F

C. pictoides. Male. Keppel I., Qld, Australia. Depth 7 m. Length 11 cm.

Australian Comb Wrasse *Coris picta*

Coris picta Bloch & Schneider, 1801.
NSW, Australia.

Subtropical eastern Australia to southern Coral Sea and northern New Zealand region. A common NSW species, where found on sand and rubble along reef margins, often forming aggregations as adults. Juveniles solitary along rocky ledges and in crevices. Acts as a cleaner wrasse at all stages. Readily identified by their black and white colour and the yellow caudal fin when adult. Length to 24 cm.

C. picta. Female. Montague I., NSW, Australia. Depth 16 m. Length 22 cm.

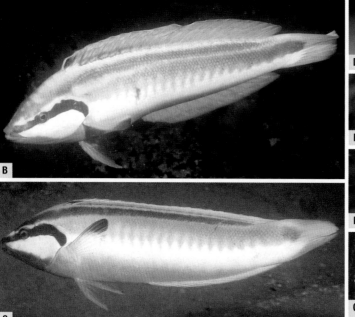

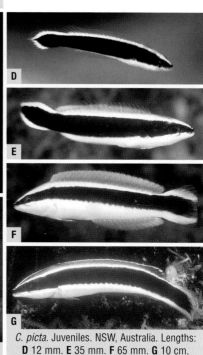

C. picta. Nuptial males. Seal Rocks, NSW, Australia. Depth 12 m. Length 24 cm.

C. picta. Juveniles. NSW, Australia. Lengths: **D** 12 mm. **E** 35 mm. **F** 65 mm. **G** 10 cm.

C. picta. Females. Montague I., NSW, Australia. Depth 25 m. Length 15–22 cm.

C. picta. Females and nuptial male (centre). Montague I., NSW, Australia. Depth 25 m. Length 15–24 cm.

Japanese Comb Wrasse *Coris musume*

Julis musume Jordan & Snyder, 1904. Japan.

Sub-tropical region of Japan, ranging south to western Taiwan. Occurs on rocky substrates with sand, rubble and low algae growth. Juveniles are active cleaners and adults may also engage in such activities with large pelagics. Readily identified by its distinctive colouration at all stages. Closely related to *Coris picta* from Australia and New Zealand. Length to 25 cm.

C. musume. Toba Aquarium, Japan. Length 12 cm.

C. musume. Kochi, Japan. **B** Juvenile. Depth 20 m. Length 4 cm. **G** Female. Depth 52 m. Length 20 cm. **F & G** Tomonori Hirata.

C. musume. Japan. **D** Oshima. Juvenile. Depth 35 m. Length 5 cm. **E** Izu Pen. Nuptial male. Depth 30 m. Length 24 cm.

C. musume. Kochi, Japan. **F** Subadult. Depth 25 m. Length 7 cm. **G** Male. Depth 52 m. Length 25 cm. **F & G** Tomonori Hirata.

Masculine. Type species: *Hologymnosus fasciatus* Lacepède, 1801 (= *H. doliatus*). A small tropical Indo-Pacific genus with 4 species, 2 of which are widespread but with some geographical variations, and 2 restricted to the West Pacific.

1 *Hologymnosus annulatus* (Lacepède, 1801) **Ringed Wrasse** (p. 173)
2 *Hologymnosus doliatus* (Lacepède, 1801) **Narrow-banded Wrasse** (p. 172)
3 *Hologymnosus longipes* (Günther, 1862) **Pale slender-wrasse** (p. 171)
4 *Hologymnosus rhodonotus* Randall & Yamakawa, 1982 **Red Cigar-wrasse** (p. 171)

These species are much like those in the genus *Coris,* but are more elongate and have a much higher scale count. They are typically found on sand and rubble adjacent to reefs, often forming small aggregations when juvenile, swimming close to the substrate in search of small benthic invertebrates. Females are often found swimming with other fish that feed on the substrate (disturbing it to dislodge prey), such as goatfish or snappers, and form small loose aggregations. Usually a single large male claims a large section of reef, from which other males are excluded, and he visits the females in his area on a regular basis, usually showing his nuptial colours for a brief moment. Juveniles expatriate to subtropical zones, suggesting a long pelagic larval stage. Settling post-larvae juveniles are about 24 mm long, which is large compared to some of the *Halichoeres* or *Macropharyngodon* species that are often well short of 20 mm.

Juveniles do well in captivity and accept all kinds of meat-based foods. They require some open spaces and fine sand to bury themselves in at night. They grow to a moderately large size and do well in community aquariums.

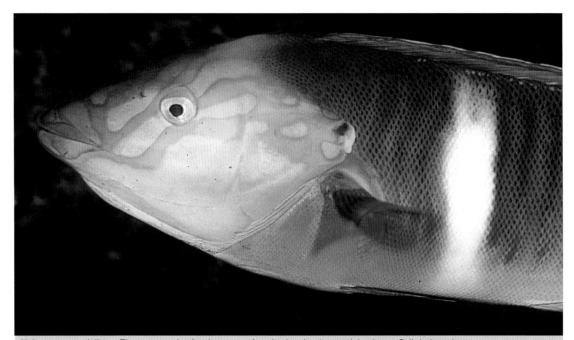

Hologymnosus doliatus. The type-species for the genus. A male showing its nuptial colours. Bali, Indonesia.

When courting and displaying to females, the male's general colouration intensifies with electric blue yellow and green. A white bar is quickly turned on and off for the occasion. This species is widespread throughout the Indo-West Pacific and shows little variation in colour - even the nuptial colours have the white bar in the same place. However, the other widespread species, *H. annulatus*, displays with a white bar that is positioned above the anus in the Red Sea and western Indian Ocean, but instead of the bar, the caudal peduncle turns white in the West-Pacific populations, suggesting that they are different and perhaps sub-specific.

Red Cigar-wrasse *Hologymnosus rhodonotus*

Hologymnosus rhodonotus Randall & Yamakawa. 1988. Okinawa, Japan.

West Pacific, Japan to north-western Australia. Few specimens reported from the Philippines and Indonesia near Wallace's Line. Occurs mainly on deep slopes with coralline algae and rubble. Juveniles with 5 red longitudinal lines. Adults mostly bright red with a distinct 'ear' spot, whitish below. Length to 32 cm.

A

H. rhodonotus. Kochi, Japan. Depth 25 m. Length 13 cm. Tomonori Hirata.

B

H. rhodonotus. Kochi, Japan. D. 25 m. L. 10 cm. T. Hirata.

C

H. rhodonotus. Hibernia R., WA. D. 30 m. L. 8 cm. Jerry Allen.

D

H. rhodonotus. Hibernia Reef, WA. Depth 30 m. Length 15 cm. Jerry Allen.

Pale Slender-wrasse *Hologymnosus longipes*

Coris longipes Günther, 1862. Vanuatu.

Coral Sea and Great Barrier Reef to Fiji, juveniles expatriate south to Montague Island, NSW. Clear oceanic waters, found on rubble and sand near rocks or corals to about 30 m depth. Forms small aggregations and often mixes with other *Hologymnosus*. Juveniles with 3 red longitudinal lines of even width. Adults have a dusky mid-lateral stripe and males have an eye-side black spot on their sides below spinous dorsal. Length to 38 cm.

A

B

C

H. longipes. Montague Island, NSW. Depth 15 m. Length 35 mm.

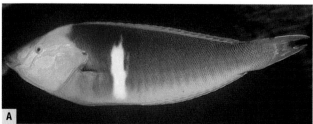

A

H. doliatus. Nuptial male. Flores, Indonesia. Depth 20 m. Length 30 cm.

Narrow-banded Wrasse *Hologymnosus doliatus*

Labrus doliatus Lacepède, 1801. Mauritius.

Widespread Indo-West Pacific, ranging to subtropical zones. Coastal to outer reefs, usually on deep slopes and large adults along drop-offs. Small juveniles on rubble zones bordering reefs onto sand. Juveniles and females usually in small groups. Males solitary and territorial, patrolling large sections of reefs. Length to 35 cm.

B

H. doliatus. Maldives. Depth 25 m. Length 14 cm.

C

H. doliatus. Sydney, Australia. D. 10 m. L. 35 mm.

D

H. doliatus. Female. NSW, Australia. Depth 22 m. Length 24 cm.

E

H. doliatus. Female. Flores, Indonesia. Depth 15 m. Length 28 cm.

F

H. doliatus. Nuptial male. Bali, Indonesia. Depth 25 m. Length 30 cm.

Ringed Wrasse *Hologymnosus annulatus*

Labrus annulatus Lacepède, 1801. Indo-Pacific Ocean.

Indo-West Pacific, ranging to subtropical zones. Two colour forms: Indian Ocean and Red Sea, and its sibling in the Pacific regions. Coastal to outer reef crests, on rubble and sand patches. Females look almost black. Males mainly greenish with blue face, with Indian form showing a white band central to the body, whilst the Pacific form have a pale peduncular area during their nuptial modes. Length to 40 cm.

A *H. annulatus*. Kerama, Japan. Depth 25 m. Length 35 cm.

B *H. annulatus*. Sydney, Australia. D. 25 m. L. 45 mm.

C *H. annulatus*. Flores, Indonesia. Depth 10 m. Length 20 cm.

D *H. annulatus*. Male. Bali, Indonesia. D. 25 m. L. 38 cm.

E *H. annulatus*. Muiron Is., Western Australia. Depth 9 m. **E** Female. Length 30 cm. **F** Nuptial male. Length 40 cm.

F

G *H.* cf *annulatus*. Variation. Nuptial male. Egypt, Red Sea. Depth 20 m. Length 35 cm.

Feminine. Type species: *Julis (Halichoeres) heteropterus* Bleeker, 1857. A small tropical Indo-Pacific genus with 5 species, 2 of which are widespread, and 3 are restricted to the West Pacific.

1 *Pseudocoris aurantiofasciata* Fourmanoir, 1971 **Rusty-banded Wrasse** (p. 178)
2 *Pseudocoris bleekeri* (Hubrecht, 1876) **Yellow-band Wrasse** (p. 176)
3 *Pseudocoris heteroptera* (Bleeker, 1857) **Torpedo Wrasse** (p. 177)
4 *Pseudocoris ocellata* Chen & Shao, 1995 **Taiwan Torpedo-wrasse** (N.A.)
5 *Pseudocoris yamashiroi* (Schmidt, 1930) **Pink Wrasse** (p. 175)

The species look much like those in the genus *Coris,* but one of their distinguishing features is that they have lunate caudal fins as adults. They are also much more inclined to school and this behaviour is a consequence of them going into open water to feed on zooplankton. Males often feed in schools by themselves whilst females are often mixed with large groups of mixed planktivores. Most species have been observed changing colour when rising from the sea bed to open water to feed. Some juveniles and females that have distinctive patterns of bars or stripes change to a very plain colour, and vice-versa when returning to the substrate. The males of *Pseudocoris bleekeri* turn on a bright yellow patch when feeding in groups that help them to stay in close contact as a school, similarly as shown in some *Cirrhilabrus-*wrasses and fusiliers that are planktivores.

Little is known about the aquarium behaviour of most species. They have a small mouth and are rather timid. They will probably be compatible with other planktivores such as *Pseudanthias-*basslets and *Cirrhilabrus-*wrasses. They are also suitable for the invertebrate aquarium. These species require sand to bury themselves in at night to sleep.

Pseudocoris yamashiroi. Small juveniles congregating. Bali, Indonesia.

The most common and widespread species in the genus. Their pelagic larval stage is carried by currents and may settle on the substrate in sub-tropical zones, well beyond their normal breeding range.

Pink Wrasse *Pseudocoris yamashiroi*

Julis yamashiroi Schmidt, 1931. Okinawa, Japan.

Widespread Indo-West Pacific, ranging to subtropical zones. Clear coastal slopes to outer reef habitats on rubble patches and sandy areas with soft corals from about 6 m depth. Often on open sand flats with large remote bommies in depths of about 20 m. Adults form small to large schools, feeding in open water on zooplankton. Juveniles congregate on reefs, usually at depths of 10-20 m, mostly feeding on mysids. Length to 16 cm.

A

P. yamashiroi. Male. Kerama, Japan. Depth 12 m. Length 15 cm.

B

C

P. yamashiroi. Kochi, Japan. Depth 15 m. **B** Length 25 mm. **C** Length 4 mm. **B** & **C** Tomonori Hirata.

D

G

E

P. yamashiroi. Sydney, Australia. D. 5 m. L. 45 mm.

H

F

P. yamashiroi. Flores, Indonesia. D. 6 m. L. 75 mm.

P. yamashiroi. **G** & **H** Males. Bali, Indonesia. Depth 12 m. Length 15 cm.

I

J

P. yamashiroi. Variation. Maldives. Depth 10 m. **I** Females. Length 65 mm. **J** Male. Length 15 cm.

Coris bleekeri Hubrecht, 1876. Ceram Island.
Coris philippina Fowler & Bean, 1928. Philippines.

Indonesia, Bali and Moluccens seas to southern Japan. Coastal sand and rubble reef, usually flat substrate with remote coral bommies in current zones. Mixes with various other fishes in open water to feed on zooplankton. Males distinctive with a bright yellow band or blotch over the body. Female plain green with black 'ear' spot and similar spot on base of caudal fin. Length to 15 cm, usually to 14 cm, growing slightly larger in cooler waters in Japan.

P. bleekeri. Males, female above in **B**. Bali, Indonesia. D. 5 m. L. 14 cm.

P. bleekeri. Juveniles. Aquarium imports from the Philippines. Length 55–60 mm.

P. bleekeri. Males. Japan. **E** Kerama. Depth 12 m. Length 13 cm. **F** Kochi. Depth 25 m. Length 15 cm. Tomonori Hirata.

P. bleekeri. Male. Bali, Indonesia. Depth 20 m. Length 12 cm.

Torpedo Wrasse *Pseudocoris heteroptera*

Julis (Halichoeres) heteropterus Bleeker, 1857. Ambon.

Widespread Indo-West Pacific, sporadic distribution between southern Japan, north-eastern Australia and west Indian Ocean, but doubtful that the latter is the same. Clear coastal to outer reef crests, usually at a few metres depth but may feed far from reefs in open water in pursuit of plankton along deep slopes. Females in small groups, usually with a male nearby. Colour changes quickly from when swimming near the sea bed to being in open water to feed and the striped pattern of the females fades to an even grey, making them difficult to see. Males have a variable banded pattern and this also changes greatly with mood as shown in the photographs. Length to 20 cm.

A

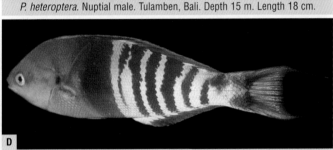

B

P. heteroptera. Nuptial male. Tulamben, Bali. Depth 15 m. Length 18 cm.

C

P. heteroptera. Bali, Indonesia. D. 15 m. L. 6 cm.

D

P. heteroptera. Male. Tulamben, Bali. Depth 5 m. Length 20 cm.

F

P. heteroptera. Aquarium. From Ribbon Reef, Qld. D. 10 m. Fenton Walsh.

E

P. heteroptera. Bali, Indonesia. D. 15 m. L. 12 cm.

G

H

P. heteroptera. Flores, Indonesia. **G** Juvenile. Depth 3 m. Length 10 cm. **H** Nuptial male. Depth 2 m. Length 18 cm.

Undetermined species.

Known from ZwaZulu-Natal and was observed by Jerry Allen in Madagascar, but is probably more widespread. Juveniles similar to *Pseudocoris heteroptera* probably a closely related species. Depth range 25–50 m. Length not known, probably about 15 cm.

P. cf *heteroptera.* **A** Male. **B** Female. **C** Juvenile. Depth 25–35 m. **A–C** Dennis King.

Rust-banded Wrasse *Pseudocoris aurantiofasciata*

Pseudocoris aurantiofasciatus Fourmanoir, 1971.
Tuamotu Archipelago.

Widespread West Pacific. Deep water drop-offs, usually along outer reef walls, usually at depths of more than 30 m. Occurs in small aggregations of females and a single dominating male. Identified by the narrow but distinct white bar on the body. Males have additional black bars with rusty brown interspaces in front, the latter turning orange during courtship. Length to 20 cm.

P. aurantiofasciata. Male. Flores, Indonesia. D. 35 m. L. 18 cm.

P. aurantiofasciata. Male. Flores, Indonesia. Depth 35 m. Length 18 cm.

P. aurantiofasciata. Male + female. Flores, Indonesia. D. 35 m. L. 18 cm.

Masculine. Type species: *Pseudojulis cerasina* Snyder, 1904. A small tropical Indo-Pacific genus with 13 species. A doubtful species from Baja California, reported as *Pseudojuloides inornatus* (Gilbert, 1890), is known only from a single specimen and needs investigation.

1 *Pseudojuloides argyreogaster* (Playfair & Günther, 1867) **Ring-cheek Slender-wrasse** (N.A.)
2 *Pseudojuloides atavai* Randall & Randall, 1981 **Polynesian Slender-wrasse** (p. 182)
3 *Pseudojuloides* cf *atavai* **Saipan Slender-wrasse** (p. 182)
4 *Pseudojuloides cerasinus* (Snyder, 1904) **Candy Wrasse** (p. 180)
5 *Pseudojuloides elongatus* Ayling & Russell, 1977 **Long Green Wrasse** (p. 184)
6 *Pseudojuloides* cf *elongatus* (Japan) **Iridescent Long-wrasse** (p. 185)
7 *Pseudojuloides* cf *elongatus* (WA) **Western Long-wrasse** (p. 185)
8 *Pseudojuloides erythrops* Randall & Randall, 1981 **Blue-head Slender-wrasse** (p. 183)
9 *Pseudojuloides kaleidos* Kuiter & Randall, 1995 **Blue-nose Wrasse** (p. 181)
10 *Pseudojuloides mesostigma* Randall & Randall, 1981 **Black-patch Wrasse** (p. 181)
11 *Pseudojuloides pyrius* Randall & Randall, 1981 **Red-face Slender-wrasse** (N.A.)
12 *Pseudojuloides severnsi* Bellwood & Randall, 1995 **Black-hat Slender-wrasse** (p. 183)
13 *Pseudojuloides xanthomos* Randall & Randall, 2000 **Yellow Slender-wrasse** (N.A.)

This genus comprises a group of small species in which males are gaudily coloured. They are usually found on deep slopes with rubble and rich invertebrate growth and coralline algae, often below outer reef drop-offs. Few species live in shallow weedy habitats. They feed on the substrate, mainly on small tube-worms that have settled on the surface of rock and algae, biting through the calcium carbonate casings. Some species were kept in the home aquarium in Sydney and were grown from juvenile to adults on a diet that primarily consisted of mysids and *Galeolaria*-worms.

Pseudojuloides cerasinus. The type-species for the genus. A pair in the author's aquarium, collected when juvenile from Montague Island, NSW, Australia. The females of most species are plain and almost identical to each other, but males are gaudily coloured and are readily identified by their distinctive markings. Males change sex and colour quickly, with complete colour changes in about 1 week.

A

P. cerasinus. Male. GBR, Australia. D. 25 m. L. 12 cm. Phil Woodhead.

Candy Wrasse *Pseudojuloides cerasinus*

Pseudojulis cerasina Snyder, 1904. Hawaiian Is.

Widespread Indo-West Pacific, with adults ranging to subtropical areas. Usually found on deep reef slopes with mixed rubble-algae habitats. Females plain pink but males with brightly coloured lines. Juveniles collected in Sydney and reared to adults in an aquarium were observed to change from pink to the male pattern in about one week. Length to 12 cm.

B

P. cerasinus. Changing sex. NSW, Australia. D. 25 m. L. 10 cm.

C

D

P. cerasinus. Montague I., NSW, Australia. Female and male in kelp habitat.

E

P. cerasinus. Kochi, Japan. Male and female. Depth 25 m. Lengths 7 & 9 cm. Tomonori Hirata.

African Candy-wrasse
Pseudojuloides cf *cerasinus*

Undetermined species

Probably restricted to the Western Indian Ocean. Previously included with *Pseudojuloides cerasinus*, but clearly represents a different and new species. Reported depth range is 15–40 m (Dennis King). Length to 12 cm.

A

B

P. cf *cerasinus*. ZwaZulu-Natal, South Africa. Male and female. Depth about 25 m. Dennis King.

180

Blue-nose Wrasse *Pseudojuloides kaleidos*

Pseudojuloides kaleidos Kuiter & Randall, 1995.
Maldives.

Indo-West Pacific, known from the Maldives to southern Indonesia as far east as Flores. Rubble slopes with mixed low algae and invertebrates, usually in current-prone channels. Juveniles and females form small groups. Males usually seen singly, moving over large sections of reef. Length to 10 cm.

P. kaleidos. Male. Maumere, Flores. Depth 25 m. Length 10 cm.

P. kaleidos. Sunda Strait. Depth 20 m. **B** Females. Length 6 cm. **C** Males. Length 9 cm.

Black-patch Wrasse *Pseudojuloides mesostigma*

Pseudojuloides mesostigma Randall, 1981. Philippines.

Only known from Southern Japan to Milne Bay, PNG, ranging along eastern Irian Jaya, but probably more widespread. Lives in very deep water, usually at depths of 30-40 m or more. Males easily recognised by a black patch centrally on the body and a black tail, but females are pink, like other species of the genus. Length to 85 mm.

P. mesostigma. Nuptial male. Milne Bay, PNG. Depth 37 m. Length 8 cm.

P. mesostigma. Kochi, Japan.**B** & **C** Depth 44 m. Lengths 40–45 mm. **D** & **E** Male. Depth 36 m. Length 10 cm. **B–E** Tomonori Hirata.

181

Polynesian Slender-wrasse
Pseudojuloides atavai

Pseudojuloides atavai Randall, 1981. Society Is.

South Pacific, Society Islands, Pitcairn, and known in Micronesia. An outer reef species that ranges to about 30 m depth. Readily identified by the colouration of both sexes. This is unlike the other members of the genus in which most females are nearly identical between species. Length to 13 cm.

P. atavai. Male. Aquarium. Origin unknown. Length 12 cm. Yutaka Niino.

P. atavai. Females. **B** Saipan. Length 10 cm. Depth 20 m. Yasuaki Miyamoto. **C** Cook Is., South Pacific. Helmut Debelius.

Saipan Slender-wrasse
Pseudojuloides cf *atavai*

Undetermined species.

This Saipan species appears to be undescribed. It is possible that the females shown in the photographs above, from the same locality, may actually be the same species, but have been reported as *Pseudojuloides atavai*. This needs to be determined by underwater observations.

P. cf *atavai.* Saipan. Male. L. 10 cm. Depth 15 m. **A–C** Yasuaki Miyamoto.

Blue-head Slender-wrasse
Pseudojuloides erythrops

Pseudojuloides erythrops Randall, 1981. Mauritius.

Only known from Mauritius and the Seychelles. Deep on offshore reefs in 50–60 m depth. Males distinguished by their blue head and white belly-patch. Females plain pinkish, identical to the next species. Length to 10 cm.

Note: Picture is of holotype.

P. erythrops. Aq. Mauritius. From depth of 57 m. Length 10 cm. Roger Steene.

Black-hat Slender-wrasse
Pseudojuloides severnsi

Pseudojuloides severnsi Bellwood & Randall, 2000. Alor I., Indonesia.

Sporadic West Pacific, southern Japan to Indonesia and aquarium specimens in Sri lanka (thought to be local). Occurs on deep slopes adjacent to drop-offs, ranging to about 50 m depth. Males identified by their distinctive colouration. Length to 11 cm.

A *P. severnsi*. Philippines. Depth 20 m. Length 11 cm. Roger Steene.

P. severnsi. Japan. **B** Kochi. Depth 42 m. Length 9 cm. Tomonori Hirata. **C** Oshima. Depth 45 m. Length 11 cm. Yasuaki Miyamoto.

P. severnsi. Oshima, Japan. **D** Depth 40 m. Length 9 cm. **E** Depth 48 m. Length 10 cm. Yasuaki Miyamoto.

P. severnsi. Male. Kochi, Japan. Depth 42 m. Length 10 cm. Tomonori Hirata.

183

Pseudojuloides elongatus Ayling & Russell, 1977. N.Z.

Disjointed populations in subtropical waters of eastern and western Australia, Lord Howe and Norfolk Island regions and intermittent occurrence in northern New Zealand. Occurs in shallow harbours as well as deeper offshore to about 25 m. Usually on rubble substrates with some outcrops of *Ecklonia*-kelp growth. Length to 13 cm, but reported to 15 cm in New Zealand, probably due to cooler conditions.

P. elongatus. Male. Aquarium. Sydney, Australia. Length 90 mm.

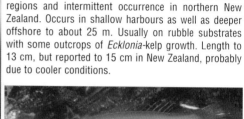

P. elongatus. Sydney, Australia. **B** Pair. Depth 2 m. Length 10 cm. **C** Juv. 45 mm. **D** Female. Depth 4 m. Length 9 cm.

P. elongatus. Australia. **E** Male. Moreton Bay, Qld. **F & G** Female & male. Lord Howe Island. D. 22 m. **E–G** Neville Coleman.

P. elongatus. Male. Seal Rocks, NSW, Australia. Length 90 mm.

Japanese Long-wrasse *Pseudojuloides* cf *elongatus*

Pseudojuloides elongatus Ayling & Russell, 1977 (in part).

Only known from subtropical Japan. Although closely related, the males differ considerably from the southern hemisphere sibling *Pseudolabrus elongatus*, like the other members in the genus, and remains without a scientific name. It occurs on rocky reefs with good algae and sparse kelp growth to about 15 m depth. Males are brightly coloured, even when not in display mood, and swim actively along the rock-faces and in gutters where the plain green to red-brown females are usually in loose aggregations. Length to 13 cm.

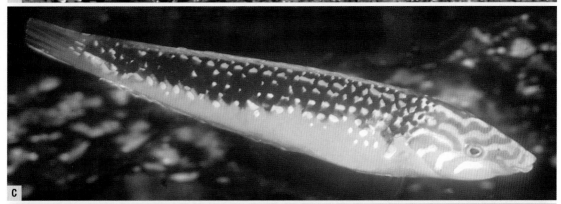

P. cf *elongatus.* Males. Izu Oceanic Park. Depth about 6–10 m. Length 12–13 cm. All different individuals.

Masculine. Type species: *Anampses cuvieri* Quoy & Gaimard, 1824. A small tropical Indo-Pacific genus with 13 species. Variously distributed throughout the Indo-Pacific with some species widespread and a few endemic to small regions.

1 *Anampses caeruleopunctatus* (Rüppell, 1829) **Diamond Wrasse** (p. 191)
2 *Anampses chrysocephalus* Randall, 1958 **Psychedelic Wrasse** (p. 194)
3 *Anampses cuvier* Quoy & Gaimard, 1824 **Pearl Wrasse** (N.A.)
4 *Anampses elegans* Ogilby, 1889 **Elegans Wrasse** (p. 196)
5 *Anampses femininus* Randall, 172) **Blue-tail Wrasse** (p. 195)
6 *Anampses geographicus* Valenciennes, 1840 **Olive-green Wrasse** (p. 189)
7 *Anampses lennardi* Scott, 1959 **Lennard's Wrasse** (p. 194)
8 *Anampses lineatus* (Randall, 1972) **White-dashes Wrasse** (p. 193)
9 *Anampses melanurus* Bleeker, 1857 **White-spotted Wrasse** (p. 192)
10 *Anampses meleagrides* Valenciennes, 1840 **Speckled Wrasse** (p. 190)
11 *Anampses neoguinaicus* Bleeker, 1878 **Black-backed Wrasse** (187)
12 *Anampses twistii* Bleeker, 1856 **Twister Wrasse** (p. 188)
13 *Anampses viridis* Valenciennes, 1840 **Green Chisel-tooth Wrasse** (N.A.)

This genus comprises a group of small to medium sized wrasse-species. Most species are beautifully coloured from the moment they settle on the bottom at their pelagic larval stage. Small juveniles often look like a floating leaf on the sea bed moved by the current, but they swim with their head down and propel themselves with their large transparent fins whilst at the same time slowly twisting their bodies. Some have a mottled pattern that makes them look like a leaf and some have large false eyes in their fins that gives them the appearance of a much larger and seemingly facing fish. They change gradually to the female stage which is usually dramatically different, and males that derive from large females are usually different again. They feed on the substrate on hard-shelled invertebrates that are noisily 'hacked' open by their chisel-like teeth. Adults often roam over shallow reef-flats in search of their prey.

Many species have been kept in captivity and most are easily kept when provided with a good layer of sand. Some species were kept in Sydney and grown from juvenile to adults on a diet that primarily consisted of mysids and *Galeolaria*-worms. Juveniles like to swim together and mixed species often do well, but they are not recommended for the invertebrate aquarium.

Anampses femininus. Montague Island, NSW, Australia. Usually the male wrasse is much more beautiful than the female, but in this species the female is just as colourful. Juvenile-*Anampses* often feature mirroring ocelli near the ends of the dorsal and anal fins. The unusual colouration and the false-eyes are a reflection of their behaviour with regards to long feeding times on the sea bed.

Black-backed Wrasse *Anampses neoguinaicus*

Anampses neoguinaicus Bleeker, 1878. Moluccas.

West Pacific, ranging from Japan along the eastern coast of New Guinea to eastern Australia, and along Wallace's line south to west Bali. Coastal and inner coral reefs along the upper part of slopes and on reef crests with *Acropora* corals. Adults occur in small loose groups of females with a dominant male nearby. Juveniles occur singly in corals. Length to 12 cm.

A

A. neoguinaicus. Male. Milne Bay, PNG. Depth 10 m. Length 12 cm.

B

C

D

A. neoguinaicus. Juveniles. NSW, Australia.
B & **C** Sydney, Depths 4–5 m. Length 24–30 mm.
D Montague I. Depth 6 m. Length 45 mm.

E

A. neoguinaicus. Female. Kalimantan, Indonesia. Depth 10 m. Length 11 cm.

F

A. neoguinaicus. Female. Milne Bay, PNG. Depth 10 m. Length 10 cm.

G

A. neoguinaicus. Male. Milne Bay, PNG. Depth 10 m. Length 12 cm.

A

A. twistii. Male. Sangihe Is., Indonesia. Depth 16 m. Length 16 cm.

Twister Wrasse *Anampses twistii*

Anampses twistii Bleeker, 1856. Ambon.

Widespread Indo-West Pacific, although the Red Sea population with a yellow head in adults, probably represents a separate subspecies. Clear coastal waters to outer coral reef flats and slopes. Usually solitary amongst large corals. Small juveniles swim with their head down, keeping dorsal and anal fins erect, and they may look like the face of a larger fish when viewed side on by a predator. Length to 16 cm.

B

C

A. twistii. Indonesia. **B** Bali. Depth 6 m. Length 12 cm. **C** Sulawesi. 7 m. Length 35 mm.

D

E

A. twistii. Kochi, Japan. Depths 6–11 m. Lengths 13 & 6 cm. T. Hirata.

F

A. twistii. Rowley Shoals, WA. 30 m. Length 30 mm.

G

A. twistii. Maldives. Depth 20 m. Length 12 cm.

H

A. twistii. Kerama, Japan. 15 m. Length 35 mm.

Red Sea Twister Wrasse
Anampses cf *twistii*
Probable subspecies

Red Sea. A mostly yellow head when adult. Apart from the yellow, it differs in colour in a number of ways, the most obvious being the series of blue iridescent spots along the scale rows on the body at an early age, as well as in large adults. Length to 15 cm.

A

B

C

A. cf *twistii*. Egypt, Red Sea. Depths 15–25 m. Lengths: **A** 12 cm. **B** 8 cm. **C** 15 cm.

Olive-green Wrasse
Anampses geographicus

Anampses geographicus Valenciennes, 1840. Indian Ocean.

Widespread Indo-West Pacific. Clear coastal to outer reef habitats with algae and soft corals in sheltered parts of reefs. Juveniles olive-green with large ocelli at the ends of their dorsal and anal fins. Adults dark green with males lacking the ocelli and having scribbled markings over the head. Usually at depths of a few to about 20 m. Length to 22 cm.

A

A. geographicus. Male. Okinawa, Japan. D. 10 m. L. 15 cm. Tomonori Hirata.

B

C

D

A. geographicus. **B** & **C** Juveniles, Sydney, Australia. Length 30–40 mm. **D** Flores, Indonesia. Depth 8 m. Length 10 cm.

A. *meleagrides*. Male. Maldives. Depth 25 m. Length 20 cm.

Speckled Wrasse *Anampses meleagrides*

Anampses meleagrides Valenciennes, 1840. Mauritius.

Widespread Indo-West Pacific. Clear coastal to outer reef habitats. Occurs at moderate depths of 10 or more metres along slopes and walls, often in soft coral or sponge habitats, but occasionally on shallow reef crests. Juveniles and females easily recognised by their white spotted body and bright yellow tail, but males are easily confused with the male *A. geographicus* when seen underwater, except when displaying with iridescent blue-green lines and spots over their body and fins. Length to 22 cm.

A. *meleagrides*. Bali, Indonesia. Depth 15–25 m. **B** Nuptial male. Length 20 cm. **C** Juvenile. Length 40 mm.

A. *meleagrides*. Male. Egypt, Red Sea. Depth 20 m. Length 20 cm.

A. *meleagrides*. Kerama, Japan. Depth 15 m. Length 40 mm. Swimming with *A. twistii*.

A. *meleagrides*. Nuptial male. Muiron I., WA. Depth 8 m. Length 22 cm.

Diamond Wrasse
Anampses caeruleopunctatus

Anampses caeruleopunctatus Rüppell, 1828. Red Sea.

Widespread Indo-West Pacific, ranging into subtropical regions. Shallow protected reefs and lagoons, often in groups on shallow rocky reef flats with mixed algae and invertebrate growth. Tiny juveniles swim with their head pointing downwards and slowly undulate their body, looking like a floating leaf in the current. Length to 35 cm, but gets larger in subtropical zones.

A

A. caeruleopunctatus. Male. Kerama, Japan. Depth 20 m. Length 25 cm.

B

C

A. caeruleopunctatus. **B** Juvenile. Sydney, Australia. Depth 3 m. Length 25 mm. **C** Maldives. Depth 25 m. Length 15 cm.

D

E

A. caeruleopunctatus. **D** Rowley Shoals, WA. Depth 6 m. Length 65 mm. **E** Female. Bali, Indonesia. Depth 4 m. Length 20 cm.

F

A. caeruleopunctatus. Male. Sangihe Islands, Indonesia. Depth 6 m. Length 35 cm.

White-spotted Wrasse *Anampses melanurus*

Anampses melanurus Bleeker, 1857. Ambon.

Widespread West Pacific, ranging west to Bali where it occurs sympatric with the Indian Ocean sibling *Anampses lineatus*). Deep coastal to outer reef slopes and drop-offs. Swims in small groups, each with several females and a single dominant male. Recognised by the yellow bar on the base of the tail. Length to 13 cm, usually to 12 cm.

A. melanurus. Bali, Indonesia. D. 20 m. L. 20 mm.

A. melanurus. **A–C** Males. Tulamben, Bali. Depth 20-25 m. Length 12 cm.

A. melanurus. Kochi, Japan. **E** Male. D. 22 m. L. 13 cm. **F** Juvenile. D. 15 m. L. 30 mm. **E & F** Tomonori Hirata.

A. melanurus. **G** Male. Kochi, Japan. D. 20 m. L. 12 cm. Tomonori Hirata. **H** NSW, Australia. Depth 16 m. Length 35 mm.

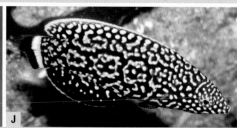

A. melanurus. Kochi, Japan. **I** Female. D. 22 m. L. 12 cm. **J** Juvenile. D. 15 m. L. 35 mm. **I & J** Tomonori Hirata.

White-dashed Wrasse *Anampses lineatus*

Anampses melanurus lineatus Randall, 1972. Red Sea.

Red Sea and Indian Ocean, ranging east to Bali, but several geographical variations. Occurs primarily on deep drop-offs along outer reefs at depths of 20 m or more. Juveniles are solitary and adults form small groups, each with several females and a dominant male. Females have a white band on the base of the tail and males have a lined pattern on the body. Males in the Red Sea have the white band. Length to 12 cm.

A

B

A. lineatus. Egypt, Red Sea. D. 20 m. L. 10 cm. Male has yellow spot.

C

A. lineatus. Juvenile. Maldives. D. 35 m. L. 35 mm.

D

A. lineatus. Female. Maldives. Depth 35 m. Length 12 cm.

E

A. lineatus. Female. Maldives. D. 35 m. L. 10 cm.

F

G

H

A. cf lineatus. Bali, Indonesia. Depth 20-25 m. **F** Male. Length 12 cm. **G** Juvenile. Length 45 mm. **H** Female. Length 10 cm.

193

Psychedelic Wrasse *Anampses chrysocephalus*

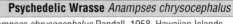

Anampses chrysocephalus Randall, 1958. Hawaiian Islands.

Endemic to Hawaiian Islands. Mainly found on ocean reefs at moderate depths. Females usually form small aggregations that are dominated by a colourful male. Juveniles and females with numerous white spots and male with blue spots on the body. Female has red on caudal fin whilst the male has an orange head with blue markings. Length to 18 cm.

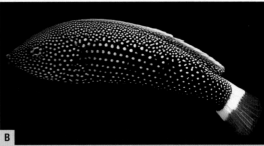

A. chrysocephalus. Aquarium. **A** Juvenile about 9 cm. **B** Female about 12 cm. **A** & **B** Yutaka Niino.

Lennard's Wrasse *Anampses lennardi*

Anampses lennardi Scott, 1959. Point Samson, WA.

Endemic to Western Australia. Known from the Exmouth region and Dampier Archipelago. Occurs on shallow reefs with mixed coralline algae and rubble substrate. Juveniles appear black with yellow over the back, but have thin white lines. Females are brilliant blue and yellow. Males have thick blue streaks on the caudal fin. A large species, reported to 28 cm.

A. lennardi. Aquarium specimens from Dampier, WA. **A** Juvenile. L. 55 mm. **B** Female. L. 25 cm. **A** & **B** Jerry Allen.

Blue-tail Wrasse *Anampses femininus*

Anampses femininus Randall, 1958.
Easter Island.

South Pacific, ranging from Australia to Eastern Island. Oceanic rocky reefs, usually in small aggregations at depths of about 20 m or more. Juveniles more shallow and solitary when small, secretive in large weeds on rocks. Females retreat to kelp when threatened. Males solitary and territorial, patrolling large sections of reef to keep other males away. Length to 12 cm.

A. *A. femininus*. Male. Aquarium grown Sydney specimen. Length 10 cm.

B. *A. femininus*. Sydney, Aus. D. 8 m. L. 25 mm.

A. femininus. NSW, Australia. **A** Solitary I. Depth 22 m. Length 12 cm. **D** Juvenile. Montague I. Depth 20 m. Length 65 mm.

A. femininus. Females. Montague I., NSW, Australia. Depth 20 m. Length 85 mm.

A. femininus. Male courting female. Aquarium grown specimens collected as juveniles in Sydney, Australia. Lengths 9–10 cm.

A. elegans. Female. Sydney, Australia. Depth 4 m. Length 20 cm.

Anampses elegans Ogilby, 1889. Lord Howe Island.

NSW, Australia, Lord Howe Island and the island region of northern New Zealand. Small juveniles amongst algae on rocks in sheltered coastal bays. At about 7–10 cm long they form small groups to cover large areas in search for small worms and crustaceans. Small groups of females are usually seen along rock and *Ecklonia* margins onto rubble substrates at moderate depths. Large males occur singly and are usually deeper, to about 30 m, sometimes checking out females in shallower water. Length to 30 cm.

A. elegans. Juveniles. Sydney, Australia. Depth 3–5 m. Lengths: **B** 45 cm. **C** 10 mm.

A. elegans. Female. Lord Howe Island. D. 4 m. L. 24 cm. Neville Coleman.

A. elegans. Juvenile. Sydney. D. 3 m. L. 20 mm.

A. elegans. Male. Lord Howe Island. D. 4 m. L. 28 cm. Neville Coleman.

Feminine. Type species: *Julis strigiventer* Bennett, 1832. A small tropical Indo-Pacific genus with 11 species. Variously distributed throughout the Indo-Pacific.

1 *Stethojulis albovittata* (Bonnaterre, 1788) **Blue-lined Ribbon-wrasse** (p. 201)
2 *Stethojulis balteata* (Valenciennes, 1839) **Belted Ribbon-wrasse** (N.A.)
3 *Stethojulis bandanensis* (Bleeker, 1851) **Red-spot Ribbon-wrasse** (p. 200)
4 *Stethojulis interrupta* (Bleeker, 1851 **Cut-ribbon Wrasse** (p. 202)
5 *Stethojulis maculata* Schmidt, 1930 **Blotched Ribbon-wrasse** (p. 203)
6 *Stethojulis marquesensis* Randall, 2000 **Marquesas Ribbon-wrasse** (N.A.)
7 *Stethojulis notialis* Randall, 2000 **Norfolk Ribbon-wrasse** (p. 202)
8 *Stethojulis strigiventer* (Bennett, 1832) **Silver-streaked Wrasse** (p. 198)
9 *Stethojulis terina* Jordan & Snyder, 1903 **Japanese Ribbon-wrasse** (p. 203)
10 *Stethojulis trilineata* (Bloch & Schneider, 1801) **Three-ribbon Wrasse** (199)
11 *Stethojulis zatima* Jordan & Seale, 1905 **Borneo Ribbon-wrasse** (p. 203)

This genus comprises a group of small species. The males typically feature iridescent blue lines along the head and body whilst the females usually have a pattern of numerous tiny spots. They form small to large groups, sometimes aggregating in very large numbers to spawn. Habitats vary between species, some preferring estuaries and lagoons and others occuring on outer reefs or in oceanic locations only, but in general they occur in shallow waters to about 15 m depth. Males are less territorial than other reef-wrasses and groups usually comprise a mixture of both sexes, although females usually greatly outnumber the males. Males are often noticeable because of their bright colours and their fast swimming using their pectoral fins. They feed mostly from the substrate, filtering small invertebrates from sand deposited amongst algae on rocks or rubble.

Some species have been kept in captivity and juveniles were grown to adult size, but proved to be more difficult than most other wrasses. They are very active and require lots of space, and suitable food has to be available at all times during the day. Most species lose condition very quickly if this cannot be provided.

Stethojulis terina. Izu Oceanic Park, Japan. Massing of females, many looking gravid and getting ready to spawn. They were observed swimming along a rocky reef in a seemingly endless stream of thousands of females with many males swimming outside the group.

197

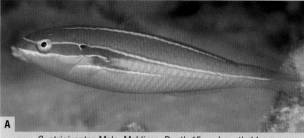

Julis strigiventer Bennett, 1832. Mauritius.

Widespread Indo-West Pacific. Coastal, algae-rich reefs, often silty lagoon habitats with seagrass beds. Swims in small aggregations over large areas. Usually shallow depths to about 15 m. Juveniles and females have silvery lines along lower sides. Males with a yellow mid-lateral band that extends to a pink-salmon band in front of the pectoral fin. Length to 12 cm.

S. strigiventer. Male. Maldives. Depth 15 m. Length 11 cm.

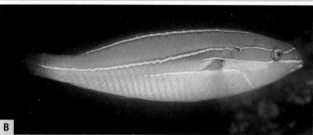

S. strigiventer. Australia. **B** Moreton Bay, Qld. Depth 3 m. Length 12 cm. **C** Juvenile. Aquarium, Sydney specimen. Length 20 mm.

S. strigiventer. Rowley Shoals, WA. **D** Male. Depth 7 m. L. 10 cm. **E** Juvenile. Depth 5 m. Length 35 mm.

S. strigiventer. Indonesia. **F** Male. Java. Depth 6 m. Length 12 cm. **G** Female. Flores. D. 3 m. L. 8 cm.

S. strigiventer. Japan. **H** Male. Kochi, D. 5 m. L. 10 cm. **I** Female. Ehime. Depth 6 m. Length 5 cm. **H & I** Tomonori Hirata.

Blue-ribbon Wrasse *Stethojulis trilineata*

Labrus trilineatus Bloch & Schneider, 1801. India.

Widespread Indo-West Pacific. Clear coastal to outer reefs. Adults usually swim in loose groups along upper parts of drop-offs or above reef crests. Juveniles and females finely-spotted, males with 3 long blue-electric lines along the body and a 4th additional one on the head which extends partly onto the body. Length to 14 cm.

A

B

S. trilineata. Pair. Flores, Indonesia. Depth 6 m. Length 14 cm.

C

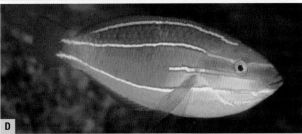

D

S. trilineata. Japan. **B** Ehime. D. 0.2 m. L. 25 mm. **C** Kochi. D. 1 m. L. 20 mm. **D** Male. Kochi. D. 2 m. L. 10 cm. **B–D** Tomonori Hirata.

E

F

S. trilineata. Females. Kochi, Japan. **E** Depth 2 m. Length 60 mm. **D** Depth 2 m. Length 7 cm. **E–F** Tomonori Hirata.

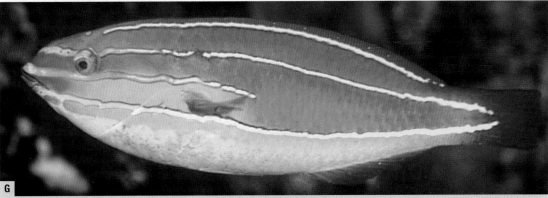

G

S. trilineata. Male. Bali, Indonesia. Depth 5 m. Length 14 cm.

Red-spot Ribbon-wrasse *Stethojulis bandanensis*

Julis (Halichoeres) bandanensis Bleeker, 1851. Banda.

Widespread West Pacific, ranging to subtropical zones. Clear coastal to outer reefs, often in small groups on exposed shallow rocky flats with low algae growth. Females mainly bluish grey with fine white spotting over upper sides and a small orange-red spot at axil of pectoral fin. Males with electric-blue lines. Length to 14 cm.

S. bandanensis. Male. Tulamben, Bali. Depth 5 m. Length 14 cm.

S. bandanensis. Male. Mabul, Malaysia. Depth 7 m. Length 14 cm.

S. bandanensis. Male. Qld, Australia. D. 6 m. L. 14 cm.

S. bandanensis. Nuptial male. Kochi, Japan. D. 3 m. L. 10 cm. T. Hirata.

S. bandanensis. Juvenile stages. Lengths from the top: 12 mm. 20 mm, 35 mm & 45 mm. **F** Kochi, Japan. T. Hirata. **E**, **G** & **H** Sydney, Australia. Depths 2–4 m.

S. bandanensis. **I** Male. NSW, Australia, D. 5 m. L. 12 cm. **J** Female. Kerama, Japan. Depth 3 m. Length 10 cm.

Blue-lined Ribbon-wrasse *Stethojulis albovittata*

Labrus albovittata Bonnaterre, 1788. No locality.

Widespread Indian Ocean, ranging to Bali where it is sympatric with its sibling *Stethojulis bandanensis*. Males lack the red axil spot of the latter and females usually feature two white lines. Shallow reef crests and clear lagoon habitats, usually in small loose groups. Length to 14 cm.

A

S. albovittata. Male. Maldives. Depth 9 m. Length 12 cm.

B

S. albovittata. Maldives. D. 12 m. L. 6 cm.

C

S. albovittata. Bali. D. 6 m. L. 10 cm.

D

S. albovittata. Female. Maldives. Depth 9 m. Length 11 cm.

E

S. albovittata. Male. Maldives. Depth 9 m. Length 142 cm.

F

S. albovittata. Female. Tulamben, Bali. D. 6 m. L. 10 cm.

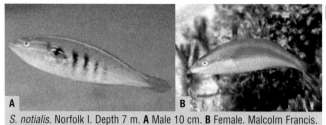

A

B

S. notialis. Norfolk I. Depth 7 m. **A** Male 10 cm. **B** Female. Malcolm Francis.

Norfolk Ribbon-wrasse *Stethojulis notialis*

Stethojulis notialis Randall 2000. Fiji.

Fiji to New Caledonia and Norfolk Island. Occurs in small groups of females, usually accompanied by a single male, on semi-open substrate with algae-rubble. Closely related to *Stethojulis interrupta* and *S. maculatus* from Japan. In the latter the dark lateral blotches extend upwards. Length to 11 cm.

Cut-ribbon Wrasse *Stethojulis interrupta*

Julis (Halichoeres) interruptus Bleeker, 1851. Banda.

Indo-West Pacific, Indonesia to Australia and to South Africa. Several geographical variations elsewhere, some of which are probably separate species. Mainly in continental regions. Coastal to outer reef crests. Occurs in small groups, usually to about 20 m depth. Juveniles on algae-rock reefs. Typical male-form has 'interrupted' mid-lateral stripe. Large individuals with dusky blotches as shown in **B**. Length to 12 cm.

A

S. interrupta. Male. Bali, Indonesia. Depth 5 m. Length 10 cm.

B

S. interrupta. Male. Sydney, Australia. Depth 6 m. Length 12 cm.

C

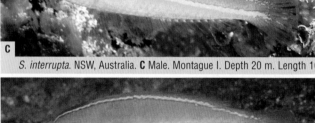

D

S. interrupta. NSW, Australia. **C** Male. Montague I. Depth 20 m. Length 10 cm. **D** Females. Bondi. Depth 20 m. Length 10 cm.

E

F

S. interrupta. NSW, Australia. **E** Male. Coogee. Depth 5 m. Length 10 cm. **F** Juvenile. Seal Rocks. Depth 5 m. Length 60 mm.

G

H

S. interrupta. Variation. Egypt, Red Sea. Depth 6 m. **G** Male. Length 12 cm. **H** Juvenile. Length 45 mm.

Blotched Ribbon-wrasse *Stethojulis maculata*

Stethojulis maculatus Schmidt. 1930. Japan.

Appears to be restricted to the more northern islands of the Ryukyu group. Males are readily identified by the large black blotch on their sides that divide into four ventrally. Female similar to *Stethojulis zatima,* but the line from the snout running onto the body is completely yellow. Length to 12 cm.

S. maculata. Male. Ogasawara I., Japan. Yusuke Yoshino.

Full-ribbon Wrasse *Stethojulis zatima*

Stethojulis zatima Jordan & Seale, 1905. Philippines.

Philippines to Malaysia and Kalimantan, replacing the closely related *Stethojulis interrupta.* Female with yellow stripe from the tip of the snout to just past axil, running below eye where stripe is pale silvery-blue. Male with continuous mid-lateral line and dark 'ear'. Length to 12 cm.

A

B

C

S.zatima. **A & B** Mabul, Malaysia. D. 10 m. **A** Male. L. 11 cm. **B** Female. L. 8 cm. **C** Male. Derawan, Kalimantan. D. 15 m. L. 12 cm.

Japanese Ribbon-wrasse *Stethojulis terina*

Stethojulis terina Jordan & Snyder, 1902. Japan.

Subtropical Japan to Taiwan. Coastal rocky reefs with kelp or other large weeds. Forms small to very large aggregations, ranging to about 25 m depth, usually swimming over sand or rubble gutters. Readily identified by its distinctive colouration at the different stages. Length to 14 cm, usually 12 cm.

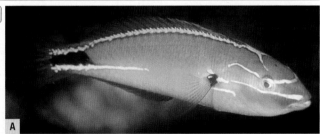

A

S. terina. Male. Izu Oceanic Park, Japan. Depth 10 m. L. 12 cm.

B

C

S. terina. Japan. **B** Juveniles. Kochi. D. 5 m. L. 35 mm. Tomonori Hirata. **C** Male. Oshima. D. 15 m. L. 11 cm.

D

E

S. terina. Gravid females. Izu Oceanic Park. Depth 10 m. Lengths 9 cm.

Masculine. Type species: *Mulles fasciatus* Thunberg, 1795. A small tropical Indo-Pacific genus with 3 species. Two are distributed throughout the Indo-Pacific and one is endemic to the Red Sea.

1 *Hemigymnus fasciatus* (Bloch, 1792) **Banded Thicklip** (this page)
2 *Hemigymnus melapterus* (Bloch, 1791) **Half-and-half Wrasses** (p. 205)
3 *Hemigymnus sexfasciatus* (Rüppell, 1835) **Red Sea Banded Thicklip** (p. 205)

The adults have thick, fleshy lips and are deep-bodied compared to most of the larger wrasses. They are mostly seen singly along reef margins on rubble and sand substrates. Small juveniles on rubble reefs, often with long-spined urchins, swimming with their heads down and slowly twisting their bodies. These are nice fish for the aquarium and go through some interesting colour changes with growth. Unfortunately they may outgrow their home and need a larger aquarium. They feed on a variety of small invertebrates and adults are often seen taking a mouthful of gravel or sand to filter for prey.

A
H. fasciatus. Maldives. Depth 20 m. Length 35 cm.

Banded Thicklip *Hemigymnus fasciatus*
Labrus fasciatus Bloch, 1792. No locality.

Widespread Indo-West Pacific. Coastal to outer reef slopes and drop-offs. Juveniles secretive on inshore reefs. Large adults swim openly on reefs, singly or in small loose aggregations. Several colour phases with age and sex. Females with 4 distinct white bars, black ventral fins, and a yellow-orange caudal fin. Males with ornamental patterns on the head that change colour during courtship. Length to 45 cm.

B
C
H. fasciatus. Australia. **B** Lizard I., Qld. Depth 15 m. Length 20 cm. **C** Sydney. Depth 4 m. Length 30 mm.

D
H. fasciatus. Padangbai, Bali. Depth 15 m. Length 45 cm.

Half-and-Half Wrasse *Hemigymnus melapterus*

Labrus melapterus Bloch, 1791. No locality.

Widespread Indo-West Pacific, ranging to subtropical zones as expatriates. Coastal to outer reef slopes and drop-offs. Juveniles occur inshore and large adults in deeper water. Usually seen solitary. Colour varies drastically with age and sex, green when very young with a main white bar developing behind pectoral fin and then changing to the white-black pattern (**B**) from about a length of 7 cm to sub-adult. Length to 50 cm.

H. melapterus. Java, Indonesia. D. 6 m. L. 45 cm.

H. melapterus. Flores, Indonesia. D. 6 m. L. 15 cm.

H. melapterus. Rowley Shoals, WA. D. 6 m. L. 40 cm.

H. melapterus. Juveniles. **D–F** Sydney, Australia. **G** Maldives. Lengths from left to right: 10 mm, 15 mm, 25 mm, & 50 mm.

Red Sea Banded Thicklip
Hemigymnus sexfasciatus

Halichoeres sexfasciatus Rüppell, 1835. Red Sea.

Endemic to the Red Sea. Occurs on rubble reefs, usually seen solitary. Juveniles dark green, with 6 white bars that widen with age. Females mainly black with 6 white bars, the first expanding over the cheek, the ventral fins white, and caudal fin black with white bar on the base. Males with additional pink markings on the head. Length to at least 40 cm, probably reaching 45 cm.

H. sexfasciatus. **A** Juvenile. Length 75 mm. **B** Female. Egypt, Red Sea. Depth 10 m. Length 35 cm.

OTHER BOOKS
IN THIS SERIES...

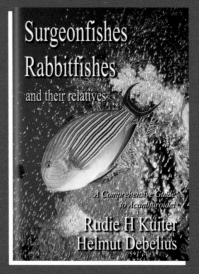

Seahorses, Pipefishes and Their Relatives
A Comprehensive Guide to Syngnathiformes
by Rudie H Kuiter

- Detailed information on over 350 different species.
- More than 1000 spectacular photographs, most taken in the fishes' natural habitats.
- Everything known about habitats and behaviour, including details of ideal aquarium set ups for each species.
- Pictured contents pages allowing information to be found quickly and easily.
- List of all known species of the World.
- Comprehensive index.
- 240 pages. Hardback.
- ISBN 0-9539097-0-0

Surgeonfishes, Rabbitfishes and Their Relatives
A Comprehensive Guide to Acanthuroidei
by R H Kuiter & H Debelius

- Detailed information on the families, genera and more than 100 known species of the world.
- Illustrated with more than 750 spectacular underwater photographs.
- Information on behaviour, habitats and details of aquarium set ups for the various groups.
- Picture index pages for visual quick-find of species.
- Comprehensive index of common and scientific names of families, genera and species.
- 208 pages. Hardback.
- ISBN 0-9539097-1-9